Clocks and Watches of the Qing Dynasty
--From the Collection in the Forbidden City

清宫钟表集萃
——北京故宫珍藏

FOREIGN LANGUAGES PRESS
外 文 出 版 社

Compiled by: Liao Pin
Text by: Lang Xiuhua, Qin Xiaopei
Photos by: Hu Chui, Liu Zhigang, Zhao Shan, Zhao Xiaoquan,
　　　　　　Feng Hui, Xia Jing, Zou Yiwei, Yu Zhiyong
Translator: Huang Youyi, Cong Guoling, Hao Guangfeng
English reviser: Paul White
Designer: Lan Peijin, Yuan Qing
Editor: Lan Peijin

First Edition 2002
Second Printing 2008

Clocks and Watches of the Qing Dynasty
　　--From the Collection in the Forbidden City

ISBN 978-7-119-03050-0

©Foreign Languages Press

Published by Foreign Languages Press

24 Baiwanzhuang Road, Beijing 100037, China

Home Page: http://www.flp.com.cn

E-mail Addresses: info@flp.com.cn
　　　　　　　　 sales@flp.com.cn
Distributed by China International Book Trading Corporation

35 Chegongzhuang Xilu, Beijing 100044, China
P.O.Box 399, Beijing, China
Printed in the People's Republic of China

Foreword

The Palace Museum in Beijing, the largest museum in China, has in its collection some of the finest clocks and watches produced worldwide during the 18th and 19th centuries. They are not only timekeeping instruments, but also examples of superb craftsmanship, testifying to the outstanding skill of clock and watch makers in both China and other countries.

China boasts a long history of the development and production of timepieces. During the 10th and 14th centuries, China invented different kinds of astronomical devices which combined the functions of astronomical measurement with the mechanical recording of time. The earliest time-measuring devices first appeared in China more than 3,000 years ago.

Ancient Chinese Chronometers

The sundial is the earliest and most primitive form of timepiece known to man. In China, the first sundials appeared during the Western Zhou period, some 3,000 years ago. The device consisted simply of an erect pole, and people tried to calculate the occurrence of the summer and winter solstices by observing the movement and length of the shadows of the pole cast by the sun. On the day of the winter solstice, the shadow was the longest, while at the summer solstice it was at its shortest. An improvement on this crude device was the gnomon, which consisted of a vertical pole fixed to a horizontal ruler marked at regular intervals. The shadows cast by the pole could be more accurately measured by using the gnomon.

A further improvement was a sundial which told the time throughout the day (The 24 hours were divided into 12 units, while each of these units was again divided into eight sub-units, equivalent to quarters of an hour) as the position of the sun shifted. It consisted of an obelisk standing on a huge stone disc engraved with the eight sub-units in each of the twelve units representing the passage of the day. This type of timepiece appeared before the Han Dynasty (206-220 BC). One made of white marble can be seen on the open terrace in front of the Hall of Supreme Harmony in the Forbidden City in Beijing. Its very location symbolizes that the emperor had under his control the unified time-telling system for the whole empire.

As the sundial relied on the sun to tell the time, it was useless on cloudy days and during the night. To solve this problem, the water clock, or clepsydra, was invented. This instrument enabled the passage of time to be observed as the level of water, the speed and amount of feed of which had been preset, rose. Water clocks varied in structure according to the times in which they were produced, but mainly they consisted of a tank from which water dripped and a container which received the water. They also ranged from mono-container to multi-container types. The water clocks of the Han

Dynasty all had a single, round water container with a movable arrow marking the change in water level. Such containers were not large enough to contain enough water for a whole 24-unit cycle and had to be refilled to keep on working. The volume on astronomy in *The History of the Song Dynasty* records details of a water clock made by Shen Kuo (1031-1095). This clepsydra consisted of three containers for relaying the water, called the *qiu hu* (initial container), the *fu hu* (second container) and the *fei hu* (last container), respectively, in addition to one for collecting water called the *jian hu*. When the containers for relaying water were filled in succession, the water flowed evenly into the one for collecting water, in which an arrow would rise along with the water level, indicating the passage of time. In the Hall of Celestial and Terrestrial Union in the Forbidden City is a large copper clepsydra 588.8 cm high, built in 1744.

Ancient Mechanical Time-telling Devices

The first mechanical timepiece in China appeared during the Han Dynasty. In the early years of the 2nd century, Zhang Heng, an imperial astronomer of the Eastern Han Dynasty, built an armillary sphere powered by water. Motivated by cog wheels pushed by dripping water, his armillary sphere turned one circuit each week in a regular fashion. Fixed to it was a mechanism indicating the number of days in the month. This consisted of an axle which turned one circuit each day. The axle, making use of the gear and cam systems, indicated the number of days in a given month in imitation of the blossoming of a legendary flower which was believed to blossom from the first to the 15th day of the month and each day bear a fruit. From the 16th day onward, it was said, a fruit would drop from it every day. At a time when there was no time-telling equipment, people observed the blossoming and withering of the flower to learn which given day of the month it was. The armillary sphere had an iron axle in the center, which revolved in the direction of the turning of the earth. The axle joined the sphere in line with the north and south poles. As it turned, it could accurately demonstrate astronomical changes.

Scientists in later times also made armillary spheres which mostly used water power. Of course, there were improvements and new creations. In 725, Zhang Suihe, a monk, and Liang Lingzan built a water-powered astroscope which had an automatic time-telling mechanical structure. Two wooden figures were fixed to a horizontal beam. One figure's job was to beat a drum for telling the time at the point of arrival of each of the eight sub-units, while the other did the same at the point of arrival of each of the 12 units in a day.

The water-driven astronomical clock tower built in 1086 by Su Song and Han Gonglian was an instrument combining an armillary sphere with a celestial globe and a mechanical timepiece. The top level is an armillary sphere, the middle part is a celestial globe, and the lower part is a five-story wooden pavilion type of structure with a door on each level. In all, more than 100 small wooden figures are fixed to the five-story pavilion. At the right time, one figure comes out of each of the doors indicating the time written on a wooden tablet held in its hand. The whole device is made up of over 150 parts. Behind the wooden pavilion is a mechanical system powered by water, which is very close to the escape device in clocks and watches of modern times. It is thus of great significance in the history of clock and watch making. In fact, it was this that prompted the British scientist Joseph Needham to conclude that it was highly possible that the tradition of Chinese astronomical clocks was the direct forerunner of European astronomical clocks of the Middle Ages.

In 1276, a time-telling device fixed to a lamp, produced by astronomers of the Yuan Dynasty, was no longer a part of astronomical apparatus, but purely a timepiece. At the turn of the Yuan and Ming dynasties (late 14th century), Zhan Xiyuan invented a five-wheel device using dripping sand, bringing clock making to the stage of telling the time with a dial plate and needles. It was an independent mechanical timepiece, similar to the chime clocks of modern times. If more efforts had been made in this direction, replacing the power produced by constant water or sand flow with that created by hammers and spiral power springs, clock making in China would have been quickly knocking at the door of modern clock and watch making and have given the technology of timepiece making a great leap forward. Since the long-lasting feudal society in China maintained a social structure of a self-sufficient natural economy and patriarchal rule marked by highly centralized power, productivity was held in check, while science and technology, which are really the primary productive forces, were given insufficient attention. In fact, technology was regarded by the rulers as a set of heretical and sinister skills, and efforts were made to suppress it. An astronomical device carved out a piece of crystal presented to the first emperor of the Ming Dynasty by an official in charge of celestial observation was smashed to pieces, as the emperor regarded it as something totally useless. Many similar inventions and discoveries made by Chinese scientists were thrown by the wayside, as they could not circulate or be made use of.

Westerners Who Introduced Clocks to China, and Clock Making in China in Recent Times

Contemporary mechanical clocks were introduced to China toward the end of the Ming Dynasty (1368-1644), when Western traders and colonizers made their way east, and large numbers of missionaries arrived in China, including the two Italians Michele Ruggieri and Matteo Ricci (1552-1610). It was Ricci who introduced clocks from the West to China.

Matteo Ricci was fluent in Chinese, and well-versed in mathematics and astronomy. He was also able to make sundials and clocks. He landed in Guangzhou in 1581, and lived in China for more than twenty years. In 1598, he went to Beijing, and three years later entered the Forbidden City, when he presented Emperor Wanli (1573-1620) with two chime clocks and a triangular prism. One of the clocks was said to have been placed in the Imperial Garden in the Forbidden City, and the other was kept in the palace halls for the use of the emperor. Since no one at the court understood the technique of clock striking, Ricci was made to stay. These two clocks had quite an impact on mechanical clock making in China. According to contemporary documents, timepieces made with hammers and spiral springs repeatedly appeared in China in the middle and later parts of the 17th century.

After Emperor Kangxi (1661-1722) of the Qing Dynasty decided to lift the ban on maritime trade with foreign countries in 1685, British, French, Italian and Portuguese merchants began to flock to China to engage in trade. The customs of Guangdong often bought Western goods for the imperial palace. After chime clocks were introduced into the Forbidden City, time there was kept accordingly. Emperor Kangxi, who was very interested in Western studies, showed a great interest in chime clocks, often taking them apart to study their structure. He even wrote a poem about how he enjoyed studying chime clocks.. According to records of tributes the imperial court received, the number of clocks brought in by Western merchants increased quickly after 1759. The Guangdong customs administration alone sent 40 to 50 clocks to the court each year. The total number of such clocks was 1,025, and most of them were made in Britain.

The Office of Manufacturing at the Hall of Mental Cultivation, a place in the Forbidden City for producing things required by the emperors also made chiming clocks. The workshop that produced chiming clocks during the reign of Emperor Yongzheng (1723-1735) was called the Clock Workshop, which employed foreigners to teach the workmen their skills. The first of these foreign experts was a Swiss named Stadlin, and many others were Western missionaries. The clocks favored by the Qing court were quite ornate, with musical functions, movable figures, sailing boats, blooming flowers, etc.

At the same time, clock making also made headway in Guangzhou and in cities along the Yangtze River such as Suzhou, Nanjing and Yangzhou.

In the period from 1736 to 1795, when Emperor Qianlong was on the throne, clocks were ubiquitous in the halls of the Forbidden City and other royal palaces. Huge numbers of clocks were kept in the Xuanyuan Hall of the Yuanmingyuan Palace and at the imperial summer retreat in Rehe, a town north of Beijing. However, many valuable clocks were stolen by marauding foreign soldiers in the 19th century. A record from 1861 says, "From the Yuanmingyuan Palace, 93 large clocks, 13 small ones, 20 big watches and 182 small ones were lost." In 1900, eight allied foreign armies invaded Beijing. Such places as the Summer Palace and the Forbidden City were looted, resulting in uncountable losses. What is preserved in the Palace Museum today is only a fraction of the clocks and watches of the period of Emperor Qianlong. Those from the period immediately before and after him are even fewer. The chiming clocks presented by Matteo Ricci have disappeared without a trace.

China's Clock and Watch Manufacturing

China's contemporary mechanical clock and watch making industry began in the mid-17th century, under the impetus of the introduction of clocks and watches from the West.

After the Italian missionary Matteo Ricci presented the Ming Dynasty Emperor Wanli with two chiming clocks, Western clocks and watches came to China as gifts in a steady stream, stimulating the founding of the clock and watch making industry in the major trading cities of Guangzhou, Suzhou and Nanjing.

Emperor Kangxi had a strong interest in astronomy and the calendars, and clocks and watches from the West had a great appeal for him, more for their technical intricacies than the ornamental uses which delighted other emperors. He set up his own workshop for making clocks and watches, employing foreign technical personnel as supervisors.

Clocks and Watches Made by the Office of Manufacturing at the Hall of Mental Cultivation This office was in charge of making utensils and was known as the "Workshop of *Ruyi* (an object symbolizing blessings)," "Workshop of Gold and Jade Objects", "Casting Workshop" and "Clock Workshop." The workshop for making chiming clocks established earlier was put under the supervision of the Office of Manufacturing in 1723. In 1732, the court changed its name from "Chiming clocks Workshop" to "Clock Workshop," and made it the first independent workshop in the palace. The workshop's heyday was during the reign of Emperor Qianlong, when some 100 foreign clock and watch designers and skilled Chinese artisans worked there, turning out large numbers of all kinds of chiming clocks.

More often than not, the clocks took the shape of traditional Chinese pavilions, halls, towers and terraces. The frames of the clocks were mostly made of dark-colored hard wood, decorated with jade, ivory, gold and silver thread, enamel and rare stones which gave the clocks a luxurious and sumptuous appearance. The making of such gorgeous objects with such expensive materials naturally required the Office of Manufacturing to work in coordination with other workshops. To ensure quality, the Guangdong Customs Office was entrusted with the import of component parts, including dial plates and clock-work springs from Europe. Large-size clocks were often specially requested by emperors, designed by Westerners and finally made with meticulous improvement of the design and careful workmanship. The black lacquer and painted tower-like clock decorated with eight immortals presenting birthday gifts, for instance, was manufactured at the decree of Emperor Qianlong, who personally revised and approved the design. It took five years to design and complete the manufacturing of this clock.

Most of the large-size chiming clocks made by the Office of Manufacturing were operated by a pendulum and had a gear relay system installed. There were also "night watchman" clocks, made in accordance with the tradition of the night watchman beating his clapper to announce the passage of the night hours in ancient China. As the length of the night changed during the different solar terms, the beats had to be adjusted, and the accomplishment of this was one of the workshop's triumphs.

In the mid-Qing period, clocks made by the imperial clock workshop boasted a series of clever and beautiful designs and superb decorations. Table clocks came in many varieties, including the pagoda type, gourd type, and turning frame type, and most of them had mobile appurtenances, such as running figures, revolving flowers, miniature orchestras and fountains spouting water. In the latter, glass tubes turned, producing the effects of water spray, as well as horizontal and vertical water flow.

During the Qianlong reign period (1739-1796), a prosperous economy and workmanship which rose to new heights led to the production of a huge number of clocks, and has left with us more clocks than any other period.

Clocks and watches made in Guangzhou In 1684, Emperor Kangxi issued a decree opening up maritime trade, and thus Western clocks entered Guangzhou. According to entries in the *Annals of Guangzhou*, "Chiming clocks were originally invented in the West. They moved with a mechanical system, struck every hour day and night. People in Guangzhou started to make clocks, but their clocks could not match those from the West in delicacy." Since clocks made in Guangzhou were not as good as those from the West, Emperor Qianlong once told the Guangzhou Custom Office: "Clocks bought for the imperial court must be made in the West." As a result, clock making in Guangzhou was strongly influenced by Western techniques, bearing unmistakable European traces in design and decoration, while obtaining an artistic effect of combining the traditions of both China and the West. Taking the shape of pavilions and towers in most cases, the copper bases of the clocks were lavishly decorated with colored enamel. Their structure was very complicated, with music accompanying the hourly strikes. Interactive devices were fixed according to mechanical theories to produce coordinated movement and accurate time telling, augmented with clever gadgets which rejoiced in such titles as "immortals wishing you longevity," "happy dragon and phoenix" and "the firewood gatherer reads the classics." Such was the reputation of Guangzhou-made clocks that officials were eager to buy them to present them to the emperor.

Clocks and watches made in Suzhou In the early Qing Dynasty, clock making in Suzhou was already fairly advanced. Handicraftsmen entered the industry in great numbers, and family workshops sprang up one after another. According to the diary of a US missionary by the name of McGovern, there were more than thirty clock workshops in the city, each hiring four people on average, giving the industry a fairly large scale.

Clocks from Suzhou varied in size, but all had complicated structures. With themes such as galloping horses, archers, water fountains, miniature orchestras and "the eight immortals crossing the sea," a single clock would require several hundred or even up to 1,000 parts. Consequently, specialized workshops producing various kinds of components emerged, and specialization and division of labor rapidly promoted the industry. The Zhongrong Workshop was widely known for its choice of materials and delicate workmanship. The chimes of its clocks were especially noted for their clarity.

Suzhou was particularly famous for its table screen clocks during the 18th and 19th centuries. The compact and complicated structure, along with redwood frames made the clocks appear like Chinese decorative screens. A movement system combining the spring with a chain and a vertical gear set enabled the spring to roll up tightly and unwind steadily, raising the degree of accuracy substantially. This constituted a major invention of the time. Some leading museums in the United States, Britain and France have Suzhou table screen clocks as prized items.

China started making mechanical clocks in the 17th century. The craft reached its height during the reign of Qianlong in the 18th century, and began to decline during the 19th century. In this period, clocks were mainly produced as articles of tribute to the emperor, as well as to satisfy the demand of the nobility and rich merchants. The products were delicate, luxurious, sumptuous and extremely expensive, which severely hampered the industry's development. When the resources of the Qing court began to dry up, coupled with the influx of European clocks, the royal palace clock making workshop and those located in various cities began to go bankrupt, and the artisans gradually dispersed, bringing the Chinese clock making industry to a standstill.

However, the nearly 1,000 clocks kept in the Palace Museum for the past 200 years and more are the cream of the clock manufacturing industry in China as well as of the rest of the world, constituting a veritable treasure house. They also serve as testimony to the cultural exchanges between the traditional Chinese and Western cultures.

European Clocks and Watches, and Their Development

Chronometry arose from the science of astronomy. Its process of development was closely connected with mathematics, philosophy, chemistry, surveying, maritime navigation and machine building. Along with the upsurge of the industrial revolution, and speedy progress in science and technology, timepieces with mechanical movements were invented and grew in popularity in Europe.

European timepieces developed from the sundial and clepsydra types to mechanical clocks. Even today, there is no clear and precise record as to exactly when and who invented the technique of the mechanical clock. Mechanical clocks first appeared in the 14th century in Europe. In 1335 the Italian city of Milan saw the first mechanical chiming clocks in the world, with a monthly error of only five to ten minutes. Later, large clocks began to appear on the tops of big buildings in London, Paris and Nuremberg. At that time, clocks had neither springs nor pendulums. Their motive force came from a device consisting of a heavy hammer tied to a rope to activate the gear. The clock showed the time, but did not have a dial. The clock on the tower of Salisbury Cathedral, which is the oldest clock still in use, having been made probably in 1386, tells the time by striking. At the cathedral in Beauvais, France, there is a medieval clock which tells the time with music. It actually has three functions: calculating the passage of the hours, striking to tell the time and playing music which serves as an alarm.

The hammers which activated the earliest clocks were made of lead wrapped in copper, hanging from bow strings or silk thread. Such clocks were suitable for installing on the walls of buildings, rather than being placed on a table or the floor. It was only when weights were replaced with springs that desk clocks and watches emerged. Pendulums were invented later. Before the 18th century, clocks often had saw-tooth pendulums which had to rely on a vertical gear to balance the force of the spring. In 1510, Peter Henlein, a clock artisan of Nuremberg in Germany, replaced the heavy hammer with a spiral spring, improving the mechanism and reducing it in size. At the turn of the 15th and 16th centuries, Italy, France and Germany produced egg-shaped watches in order to make the timepiece easier to carry around. In 1583, Galileo (1564-1642), the Italian astronomer, discovered the theory of vibration of the pendulum in his workshop. Christiaan Huygens (1629-1695) of Holland improved Galileo's theory in 1656 with his theory of "swaying pendulums". Later, he created a clock regulated with a pendulum, enabling desk clocks to become a major form of timepiece and visibly raising the degree of accuracy of the clock. The appearance of pendulum clocks allowed scientists to be able to accurately study the speed of the physical processes and unfold the law of the movement of natural materials. Later, Britain, France, Germany and Switzerland became major producers of pendulum clocks.

British artisan Thomas Tompion (1638-1713) invented an I-shaped escape wheel system in 1695. Daniel Quare (1649-1724) added two needles of different lengths to the center of the dial of the clock and rendered marks indicating the hours and minutes along the edge of the dial. The longer needle indicated the minutes while the shorter one indicated the hours, a structure that is used to this very day. In 1644, British scientist Robert Hooke invented the balance spring for clocks and watches, succeeding in producing hand-held clocks easy to carry around and paving the way for the manufacturing of pocket watches. In 1757, Thomas Mudge (1715-84), also from Britain, invented a free anchor-type escapement whose appearance marked a major innovation in the technology of clock and watch making. Four years later, John Harrison, a clock manufacturer from York, Britain, produced a clock suitable for maritime navigation, which had an error of only one-tenth of a second in twenty-four hours and only three seconds in a month. In 1820, the first watch that had a separate needle for marking the seconds and that could be stopped at any time was produced in Switzerland. This was the prototype of the modern stop-watch. In 1842, Adrien Philippe produced the first watch with a winding handle. After that, a hand-held winding device replaced the original key for winding. The first wristwatch was successfully made in 1790 in Geneva, although it had certain defects. It was not until 1902 that the first mechanical wristwatch was produced. It also won the patent right for automatic winding.

After several hundred years of continuous study, experiment and improvement by artisans and scientists, clocks and watches in Europe became increasingly accurate and sophisticated. The big clock still hanging on the government building today in Copenhagen, capital of Denmark, was made with 1,400 component parts. Apart from telling the time, it also tells lunar and solar eclipses. It is so accurate that its error is only half a second in 300 years. After this clock was produced, pocket and wristwatches of great degrees of sophistication and elegance began to be made.

The most conspicuous characteristics on the surfaces of European clocks and watches are the round and bas-relief sculpture, a reflection of the sculpture art on clocks which emerged with the Renaissance. The images of human beings and animals are vivid and rendered with beautiful lines.

The collection of European clocks and watches in the Palace Museum includes ones made in Britain, France, Switzerland, Denmark and Italy. Their varied styles, graceful shapes and elegant appearance make them gems of the collections in the museum.

Clocks and Watches from Britain Along with the industrial revolution, British industry quickly progressed. Adopting mechanical processes, its clock and watch industry yielded products good in quality and great in quantity, which, apart from satisfying domestic needs were also exported. In the 13th century, the compass, which had been invented in China was introduced to Europe. At the beginning of the 14th century, the compass became universal in ocean-going vessels. As European merchants and navigators arrived in the East one after another, the clock manufacturers of Britain began to export their products to the East too.

During the reign of Qing Dynasty Emperor Shunzhi (1644-61), Westerners serving in the imperial palace presented the Chinese government with gifts brought from the West, in the hope of propagating Western culture. They also took care of and repaired the chiming clocks for the emperor and provided guidance to palace artisans in clock making. Later, the emperors, nobility and other wealthy people grew dissatisfied with locally made clocks, and demanded the more advanced and exotic foreign ones. The archives of the Qing Dynasty palace indicate that during the reign of Emperor Qianlong alone, the number of clocks purchased by the Guangzhou Customs Office and offered as tribute to the throne totaled more than 2,700. And the bulk of these clocks were made in Britain.

Britain, in fact, was one of the first countries to produce mechanical clocks and watches in bulk. In 1348, the first chiming clocks were erected in London. Earlier mechanical clocks made in Britain relied mostly on the regulation of the swaying of heavy hammers to control the escapement. They were huge in size and mostly installed in public facilities and churches. During the 14th to the 16th centuries, "grandfather" clocks and table clocks appeared, with those made by Thomas Tompion and Daniel Quare being the most sophisticated. Their long chest-shaped clocks had carved and openwork patterns on the surface. Metal plates used in the clocks were also carved with patterns. The clock Tompion made for the bedroom of William III (1689-1702) at Hampton Palace did not need winding for three months. He also made one for Buckingham Palace which did not need winding for 12 months. Unfortunately, neither of these clocks has been preserved.

During the 18th century, there were dozens of clock workshops in London. The leading makers, who engraved their names on their clocks, were Joseph Williamson, James Cox, George Higginson, William Carpenter, John Barrow, William Hughes and Benjamin Ward. There were many other clocks which were anonymous, but were equally elegant.

The Williamsons of London were traditional clock makers for generations. Joseph Williamson, who lived during the reign of Queen Anne (1702-14), invented accurate astronomical clocks and calendar clocks marked with the days and dates. His descendant, Timothy Williamson, turned out a wide range of clocks with accurate mechanical systems for telling the time and producing music, ornamented with movable figures. One of his clocks had four stories. On the top two figures held a horizontal banner wishing the beholder a long life. Underneath, a figure struck the hours. Further down, was a figure which would bend over a desk as if writing when the clock struck.

James Cox produced a huge clock between 1760 and 1765, the spring of which was motivated by air pressure. It did not need refilling with air for three months at a time. Cox was known for graceful and accurate clocks, which were put on show in a museum in London in 1772. The Cox father and son operated a clock company in Guangdong from 1783 to 1790, where they designed many desk clocks with Chinese artistry, such as a gilded square clock with a caged bird, which was a representative work of theirs. The Manchu nobles had the habit of carrying around birds in cages, and so this clock served a double purpose. When the elder Cox died in 1788, his son ran the company until 1792.

Clocks made in Britain were meticulously executed. They mostly took the forms of gilded frames, and were in classic European architectural styles of houses, churches and towers, as well as various kinds of animals. The surface was usually decorated with glass, stone and enamel materials in attractive colors. Their inner structure contained devices for telling the time, announcing it by striking or by the playing of mechanical music. Interactive gear systems motivated by springs were used to operate moving figures, animals, birds and fountains. Small pocket watches were also highly elegant, often inlaid with expensive jade and diamonds.

The British clocks kept in the Palace Museum in Beijing are both accurate timekeepers and objects of admiration. Today, such sophisticated clocks are hard to come across even in Britain. Thus they provide extremely valuable materials for the study of the history of clock making in Britain..

Clocks and Watches Made in France France was one of the first mechanical clock producers. During the 14th century, clocks appeared in public places in Paris. After a crown wheel escapement appeared in France in 1396, clock making throughout Western European gained speedy progress. In 1459, French artisans produced the first spring clock for King Charles VII. At the turn of the 15th and 16th centuries, egg-shaped watches and clocks as well as four-sided table clocks emerged in Italy, France and Germany. The

17th century saw the appearance of pendulum clocks in France. During this period, French clock artisans made a careful study of winding springs, balance springs and escapements, greatly promoting the development of clock making. After the French Revolution of the 1790s, the clock industry made extensive use of mechanical production means. Besides satisfying domestic needs, clocks and watches from France were also exported to the East. The French clocks and watches collected by the Palace Museum in Beijing are mostly products of the late 19th and early 20th centuries.

In most cases, French clocks and watches were made of metal, with colored enamel and precious stones for decoration. Many French clocks were made in the shape of churches, boats, locomotives and birdcages. They were activated either by pendulums or steel balls. Some of the timepieces contained such instruments as thermometers, anemometers, musical boxes and compasses. Some of the French clocks and watches in the Palace Museum were made in Paris, while others were made by French clock companies stationed in China.

Clocks and Watches Made in Switzerland Switzerland was a pioneer in the clock and watch making industry. In the mid-16th century, Geneva became a major clock production base, with Swiss, French and Italian artisans. Around 1700, artisans in Geneva for the first time employed a perforated ruby as a journal bearing, a trend that was afterwards widely copied. In 1786, the first automatic pocket watch was made in Geneva. This watch, which had a second hand, was the prototype for the wristwatch, which was invented four years later. In the 19th century, Switzerland was famous worldwide for its elegant and accurate clocks and watches.

Pocket watches from Switzerland were small and thin. Their shells were coated with either silver, gold or copper, inlaid with precious stones and pearls and painted with colored enamel. Apart from the normal round-shaped watches, there were also fan-shaped, lock-shaped and insect-shaped watches. Most of the clocks and watches in the Palace Museum date from the 19th and 20th centuries, including ones made by Bovet (1820-1918), Juvet (1848-91), Levy (1880-1900) and Ullmann (1893-early 20th century).

The Palace Museum also has a small collection of clocks and watches from Italy, Denmark, Japan and the US, which are also characterized by elegant and meticulous workmanship. Undoubtedly, these items were the most exquisite clocks and watches in the countries where they were made.

前 言

在中国最大的博物馆——北京故宫博物院中，收藏着18世纪和19世纪中外上佳的钟表。这些钟表不但是清代帝后日常生活的计时工具，也是精美绝伦的工艺品。它显示了那个时代中外钟表匠师的卓越才智和高超技艺。

中国计时器的发明，有着悠久的历史，在10世纪到14世纪之间，中国就创制出多种集天文仪器与机械性计时器于一体的天文钟，而古老的计时器的出现则可追溯到三千多年前。

古老的中国计时器

约在三千年前的西周初期就已发明的土圭是至今所知最原始的计时器。它只是直立在地上的一根杆子，人们凭借太阳光投射的杆影，及杆影移动的规律、影的长短，以定冬至和夏至日。冬至日的影子最长，夏至日影子最短。土圭是十分简单的计时仪器，不易掌握观察，后又逐渐发展成为圭表。圭表的构造分为两部分，直立部分叫表，横着的部分叫圭，表与圭垂直相连，以圭上的表影长短来测时。

"日晷"是一种利用太阳指示的位置以测定当时的时辰（一时辰相当于2小时）或刻数（每8刻为一时辰）。它由一根产生投影的针和一个面上刻有时刻线的晷盘组成，大约在汉代（前206－公元220年）以前就已经出现。在北京紫禁城内太和殿前的露台上有一汉白玉日晷，此日晷置于皇宫的正殿前象征着皇帝执掌全国统一时刻，取"授时"之意。

因为日晷的计时只能在有太阳的时候来测定时间，在阴天和夜间失去了作用，故而人们又创制了漏壶。漏壶是以壶盛水，利用水均衡滴漏的方法，观察壶中"刻漏"上的水位以知时间。漏壶的构造历代不尽相同，有泄水型漏壶和受水型漏壶。形制有单壶式和多壶式。汉代的漏壶都是圆筒形，是单壶泄水型沉箭漏壶，容量也都不大，一次所盛水量滴流计时还不到十二时辰。宋代沈括（1031－1095年）所制的漏壶记载在《宋史·天文志》中，是多壶式浮箭型。有播水壶三个，称求壶、复壶、废壶；受水壶一个，称建壶。注水入播水壶中后，水均衡流入受水壶，壶内刻箭随水位升高而上浮，观看箭上露出水面的刻度来计时。在故宫交泰殿内，有一大型铜壶滴漏，造于清代乾隆九年（1744年），是多壶式漏壶，通高588.8厘米。现作为一件古老的计时器在宫中陈列。

古代机械计时器

中国机械计时器最早出现在汉代。2世纪初，东汉科学家张衡制作了水力浑仪。张衡曾在东汉朝廷内两度担任执管天文的太史令，他是中国创制出机械计时器的第一人。他制造的浑仪利用漏水推动齿轮，带动浑天仪有规律地一天转一周，并加上表示每月的日数自动装置。这种装置就是每天旋转一周的轴，利用齿轮系统和凸轮机构，自动以蓂荚开落的形式计算每月的日数。"蓂荚"本是传说中的一种草木，据说它每月初一至十五日，每日生一荚；十六日以后，每日落一荚。在无计时工具的情况下，人们观察荚的开落数目，就可得知当日是一月中的哪一天。浑天仪是一球形，有一根铁轴穿过轴心，轴转动的方向就是地球自转的方向，轴和球体两个交点，就是南、北极。转动后，可以将天象准确地表现出来，这是在浑仪上以齿轮系转动计时器的最早记载。

张衡以后，历代一些科学家都制造过浑仪或浑象，也多是用水力为原动力，但均有改进和创新。如唐代开元十年（725年），一行和尚张遂和梁令瓒创制的水力天文仪器，有自动报时的机械结构，立二木人于地平之上，一人敲钟鼓报刻，一人敲钟报辰。

北宋元祐(1086－1094年) 初年苏颂和韩公廉等所创制的水运仪象台，是把浑仪、浑象和机械性计时器组合起来的一种装置。台上方置浑仪，中间置浑象，下边建五层木阁，层层有门，百余个木人分置其内，到时各门中木人执牌出来报时刻。整个水运仪象台共有150多个零件，组成一个统一的体系。木阁后装有水力发动的机械系统，这部分的构造，已相当于近代钟表上的擒纵器。在钟表发展史上有着极为重要的意义。英国科学家李约瑟据此认为："中国天文钟的传统似乎很可能是后来欧洲中世纪天文钟的直接祖先。"

元至元十三年(1276年)天文学家创制的大明灯漏计时部分已初步脱离了天文仪器的范围，专用于计时了。元末明初詹希元的五轮沙漏更达到了用表盘和指针表示时刻的阶段，发展成为独立的机械性计时器，与近代的自鸣钟相似，如果继续努力，把利用水的恒定流量或沙的力量作为动力改变为重锤和发条等器件，就可以很快敲开现代钟表的大门，使中国的计时器技术有一个飞跃。可惜的是，中国长期处于封建社会，自给自足的自然经济和宗法家族的社会结构，以及高度集权的专制主义，桎梏着生产力的发展，作为第一生产力的科学技术不仅不受重视，还被封建统治阶级视为"异端邪说"、"奇技淫巧"，竭力加以限制。如明代初年司天监进呈给朱元璋的水晶刻漏，被视为无用之物而把它击碎。许多科学家的发明创造得不到推广和流传而被埋没。

西方钟表的传人及中国近代钟表制造业

近代机械钟表是明代（1368－1644年）末期传入中国的。西方殖民主义者东进，大批传教士涌入中国，其中意大利人罗明坚（Michele Ruggieri）和利马窦（Matteo Ricci，1552－1610年），尤其是后者是把西洋钟表介绍到中国来的代表人物。

利马窦通晓中文，并精于数学、天文学，能制造日晷和钟表。他于明万历九年(1581年) 入居广州，在中国生活了20多年。1598年利马窦到达北京，于1601年进入宫廷，向明代万历皇帝（1573－1620年在位）进献了两架自鸣钟和三棱镜等，据说当时一架自鸣钟安放在御花园内，一架放置在宫内供皇帝使用。自鸣钟在运行当中，发生自撞现象，宫中没有掌握这方面技术的人才，利马窦得以留在宫中。这两架自鸣钟对中国制造机械钟有着一定的影响。据文献记载，17世纪中、下叶国内屡屡出现以重锤和发条为动力的计时仪器。

清康熙二十三年（1685年）开放海禁后，英国、法国、意大利、葡萄牙等国相继来华进行贸易，粤海关经常为皇宫购买西洋物品。西洋钟表作为商品进入中国后，皇宫内开始以钟表计时。康熙皇帝热衷于西学，对自鸣钟颇感兴趣，暇时喜拆装赏玩，并作有《戏题自鸣钟》一诗。从宫中"贡单"档案中反映，约从乾隆二十四年（1759年）后，西洋商人舶来的钟表增多，仅粤海关年贡钟表达四五十件。乾隆五十六年（1791年）由粤海关进口的大小自鸣钟等物件共1025件，从清代宫中遗留的钟表看，大多是英国钟表。

紫禁城内专为皇帝制作御用器物的"养心殿造办处"也制作自鸣钟。清雍正年间（1723－1735年）制作自鸣钟的作坊称为"做钟处"。做钟处聘用外国技师，传授技艺。瑞士人林济格（又叫斯太德林 Stadl-in），是进入皇宫中最早的一位钟表制造者，以后又有许多工匠进入做钟处，使宫内钟表业得以发展。据德国人约翰·温切尔回忆，"18世纪30年代和40年代在林济格领导下，作坊内就有100名中国人在工作"。清宫做钟处制造的钟表以用料昂贵，装饰富丽的御用钟而闻名。做钟处的主要技术人员多是西洋的传教士，他们受过良好的西方文化的教育，在他们的指导下，制造出的钟表无疑会打下西方文化的烙印，但更多的体现了宫廷皇家的好尚。清宫收藏的钟表大多带有乐曲、水法、走人、行船、开花等机械装饰，具有极强的观赏性。

与此同时，南方的广州，长江下游一带的苏州、南京、扬州等地制钟业也相继得到了发展。这样就有了"广制"和"苏制"钟表的称谓。

清乾隆时期（1736－1795年），钟表在宫廷殿宇中，比比皆是。陈设在圆明园和热河行宫等处的钟表，也为数甚巨，只是在近百年来屡遭帝国主义的侵略和掠夺，损失巨大。如咸丰十一年（1861年），清宫《奏销档》载："圆明园失落大钟93件，小钟13件，大表20件，小表182件。"1900年，八国联军进攻北京时，颐和园和中南海等处，均遭联军劫掠，损失更是不计其数。今故宫博物院所存，只为乾隆年间的一部分，康熙和雍正年间的钟表更是稀少，而明代利马窦所赠送的自鸣钟已全无踪影。

中国的钟表业

中国近代机械钟表工业始于17世纪中叶。西洋钟表的传入，使中国制钟业受到一定影响，并在结合传统制钟业的基础上逐步发展，很快达到相当规模。

1601年，意大利传教士利马窦给明朝万历皇帝送来的礼物中有两架时钟，随后西洋钟表作为馈赠礼物不断涌进，促使中国沿海广州、苏州、南京等地相继出现了自己的制钟业，到清康熙时期，机械钟的制造逐渐兴起。

康熙皇帝对天文、历法等科学十分重视，各式各样制作奇巧的西洋钟表引起他浓厚的兴趣，宫中从使用、观赏、收藏而逐步转向制造，于是在清宫养心殿造办处设"自鸣钟处"，允许西方制表技术人员在宫中供职，与中国工匠一起制作。

养心殿造办处所制造的钟表　养心殿造办处是清代内廷中内务府所属机构，又称"内务府造办处"。养心殿造办处"掌制造器用，凡制器之作有四：曰如意馆，曰金玉作，曰铸炉处，曰造钟处……"做钟处的前身为康熙年间设于内廷的自鸣钟处，雍正元年（1723年）自鸣钟处归并造办处管理。雍正十年（1732年）将自鸣钟处改名为做钟处，成为宫廷内一个独立的作坊。乾隆时，做钟处为盛鼎时期，这里聚集了技术精湛的西方钟表设计师和中国的能工巧匠近百人，制作了大量的各种类型的自鸣钟。做钟处主要是遵从帝后及宫中需要制作钟表。所制的钟表外形多为中国传统式的亭台楼阁造型，钟的基本框架多选用色调浑厚的硬质木料，以珍贵的玉器、象牙、金银丝、珐琅、石料等装饰木质表面，金镶玉嵌，使钟的外部造型富丽华贵。因此在制作过程中，就需要宫廷造办处其他作坊协作配合。为了保证钟的质量，还通过广东粤海关自欧洲购进发条、表盘等零部件。一些大型的时钟往往是皇帝直接授意，由西洋画样师设计，反复修改制作。如"黑漆彩绘楼阁群仙祝寿钟"就是按照乾隆旨意制作，并经皇帝审样修改，从设计到竣工费时五年。

做钟处制造的大型自鸣钟，大多采用以坠砣为动力源的装置带动走时、报时刻的齿轮传动系统。"更钟"是根据中国古代夜晚打更报时的传统而创造的打更钟。它的机械制造除报时报刻系统外，还增加了发更打更的齿轮系统，还有调更、定更的机构；按一年中24个节气夜间的长短变化，调整并确定更的起讫和间隔时间，做到按时准确打更。这无疑是一种创造。

清中期，宫廷做钟处制作的时钟，式样奇巧，装潢精致。有造型各异的座钟，如遥架式、迎手式、转塔式、葫芦式等等。同时，这些钟大多附设音乐、水法、跑人、转花等新颖别致的活动物体。尤以水法最为奇异，它由机械轮带动玻璃管旋转，出现了上喷水、下流水、平流水等不同效果，这时，钟的制作已不仅仅是计时，更多的是为了娱乐和陈设。

乾隆时期，由于经济繁荣，工匠技艺高超，制作钟表的数量最多，而且保留下来的精品也是最多的。

广州制造的钟表 康熙二十五年（1684年）下诏"开海禁"，此后欧洲钟表随着通商口岸开通，直接进入广州。据《广州府志》记载："自鸣钟出西洋，以索转机，机激则鸣，昼夜十二时皆然……广人亦能为之，但未及西洋之精巧。"由于广州制钟水平不及西洋，乾隆曾谕旨粤海关："购进钟表必须洋做。"因此，广州钟表业深受西方影响，许多产品在造型、图案等方面近似欧洲钟表，具有中西合璧的艺术效果。但随着钟表生产发展，工艺技术不断改进，广州的钟表业水平大大提高并制作出许多具有民族特色的产品。其造型大都是亭台楼阁式，表面装饰富丽堂皇的铜胎珐琅彩。内部构造复杂，既有走时报时伴奏，还利用机械联动原理，带动多变的玩意系统相互关联，协调动作，既能走时准确，还能有多彩的表演动作。广制钟表中尤以称颂太平盛世为题材的"群仙祝寿"、"龙凤呈祥"、"渔樵耕读"等钟表制作得活灵活现，令人赏心悦目，甚得皇帝的欢心，于是官员们纷纷以广制钟做为贡品，进献给皇帝。

苏州钟表 清初，苏州的钟表业亦相当发展，不少手工业者加入制钟行业，形成特有的"家庭式"手工业作坊。据美国传教士马克格温的记载，当时苏州制钟作坊已有30多家，每家平均有雇员4人，具有了一定的规模。

苏州钟表外形大小不一，内部结构复杂，许多钟还有走马、射箭、水法、音乐、八仙过海等装置，更显复杂。做一只钟往往要数百甚至上千种各不相同元件，故而，逐渐出现了各种零附件的专业作坊，有的做外壳，有的做机芯，而机芯中的钟碗、链条、发条、钟盘也由专人制作。如著名的张荣记制钟碗作坊，用料讲究，做工十分精细，做出的钟碗音质悦耳清澈，技艺超出同行，成为当时的名牌产品。这种专业分工，大大加速了制钟业的发展。

18世纪和19世纪时，苏州的插屏钟很出名，其钟机结构紧凑合理，钟壳都是红木框架，状似中国屏风。这种插屏钟以发条配以链条和塔轮组成动力源结构，能使发条卷紧，力量充足又能缓缓输出，十分有效地提高了钟的定时精确度，这在当时是一项重要的发明。据外国文献记载，美、英、法等国的一些著名博物馆都将苏州插屏钟作为珍品收藏。

中国机械钟表制造业，从17世纪开始，至清乾隆时期达到高峰，19世纪后渐趋衰落。当时制钟业主要生产宫廷的贡品玩物，以及满足达官贵人、富商的需求，产品要求华贵精巧，造价昂贵，故其发展受到极大局限。当清廷经济衰竭，加上欧洲钟表大量涌进，宫廷及各处做钟处随之纷纷倒闭，工匠流散，中国钟表业遂处于停滞状态。

但是，200多年来庋藏在故宫博物院的近千件钟表，是中国乃至世界钟表的精粹，是弥足珍贵的，也是中国传统文化与西方文化交融的见证。

欧洲机械钟表及其发展

钟表这门学科，最初隶属于天文学，在它的发展过程中，又与数学、物理学、化学、测地、航海和机械制造相联系。随着工业革命兴起，科学技术有了突飞猛进的发展，以机械为动力的计时器开始在欧洲兴起。

欧洲时钟经历了水钟和机械钟两个阶段。机械钟表制造业起于何时，发明人是谁，至今还未有明确的记载。大约从14世纪开始有了机械钟表。在1335年，意大利的米兰有了世界上最早的机械打点钟，走时每月误差5－10分钟。以后在英国的伦敦、法国巴黎、德国纽伦堡等高大建筑物上出现了报时钟，钟没有发条做动力，也没有钟摆来调节速度，采用的原动力是用绳索系着重锤作为带动齿轮的装置，只能走时，没有表盘。如英国索尔兹贝里市教堂大楼上的最古老的钟，现在还在使用，大约制于1386年，该钟没有表盘，而是以钟鸣来报时，这架运转了六百余年的时钟曾于1956进行过一次大修。在法国博韦大教堂内有一座古老的音乐报时大钟，具有计算、报时和音乐闹时三种功能，平时可报一刻、二刻、三刻、整点，是14世纪的音乐闹钟。法国工匠于1396年制出冠状擒纵机构。

最早的钟表动力源是由坠力发动的，坠子用铜皮灌铅制成，也即重锤。重锤用弓弦或丝绳悬起，这种钟表只适合于挂在墙壁和建筑物上，或立于地上，不能放置在桌上。把坠力的动力改为发条，才有了座钟和表，以后又发明了"行摆"。18世纪以前，钟表多为锯齿摆，所以必须加设塔轮，均衡发条的力量。1510年，德国纽伦堡的钟表工匠彼得·亨莱（Peter Henlein）把重锤改为盘簧（即发条），改善了机械时钟，并把它小型化。15世纪末、16世纪初，为便于携带，意大利、法国、德国相继研制出蛋形表。1583年，意大利著名天文学家伽利略（Galileo，1564－1642年）在实验室中发现了摆的振动等时性学说。1656年荷兰的惠更斯（Christiaan Huygens，1629－1695年）将伽利略的理论加以发展，创造了"摆钟"理论，随后又创造了以"摆"做为钟摆调速器的摆钟，从此摆钟就成为座钟的一个主要形式，使钟的走时精度提高了一大步。1657年制成的摆钟，安置在荷兰的议事堂内。摆钟的出现，使科学家有可能精确研究物理过程的速度，揭示了自然界物质运动的规律。后来，英国、法国、德国、瑞士成为摆钟的重要产地。

英国工匠托马斯·汤姆皮恩（Thomos Tompion，1638－1713年）于1695年发明了工字轮擒纵机构。丹尼尔·夸尔（Daniel Quare，1649－1724年）在机械钟盘中心安上两根长短不同的针，并沿着表盘周围刻上时、分，长针指分，短针指时，这种结构一直沿用至今。1644年英国科学家罗伯特·虎克（Robert Hooke）发明了钟表上的游丝，制造出便携式的钟表，为制造怀表创造了良好的条件。1757年，英国人托马斯·姆治（Thomas Mudge，1715－1784年），发明了自由锚式擒纵机构，它的出现标志着钟表技术的重大改革。1761年英国约克郡的钟表制造商约翰·哈里逊（John Harrison）制造出了能在海上航行所需要的钟表，每天误差只有1/10秒，连续走一个月，误差仅为3秒。1820年瑞士研制出第一只可将秒针分离出来，并可以随时停下来的表，它是现代计时器的初型。1842年阿德瑞·菲力普（Adrien Philippe）制成了第一个带有上弦把柄的钟表，从此逐渐以手柄代替钥匙上弦。最早的手表于1790年在日内瓦试制成功，但它并不完善，直到1902年第一块机械手表终于研制成功，因是自动上弦表而获得了专利。

欧洲机构钟表经过科学家和匠师们几百年的不断改进和研制，日趋精确和完善。至今仍悬挂在丹麦首都哥本哈根政府大楼上的"奥尔莱"大时钟，由1400个零件组成，可指示时间、月食、日食，走时的精确度为三百年仅差0.5秒。后来，又制造出精美的怀表和腕表。

欧洲钟表外形的最大特点是，在钟表上装饰有圆雕和浮雕，这是欧洲文艺复兴后雕塑艺术在钟表上的表现，所雕的人物和动物姿态各异，柔丽舒展，衣饰线条流畅。

故宫博物院收藏的欧洲钟表有英国、法国、瑞士以及丹麦、意大利等国制造的，这些钟表风格多样，琳琅满目，成为院中名贵的藏品。

英国钟表　英国工业革命以后，工业迅速发展，钟表制造业采用了机械制造，其产量和质量都已相当可观，在满足本国市场需求的同时，寻找向外输出的渠道。从13世纪起，中国发明的指南针已传入欧洲，14世纪开始，指南针已普遍使用，千吨的快速帆船也已出现，这就使远洋航海成为可能。《马可·波罗行纪》的广泛流传，使西方人对神话般的东方无比向往，欧洲的商人、航海家等纷纷来到东方。英国的钟表制造商也把钟表输入东方。

清代顺治年间（1644－1661年）在北京清宫供职的西洋人，为宣扬西洋的科学文化，多次献上西洋礼品，其中有"天球自鸣钟"、"大自鸣钟"等等，还为皇帝管理和修缮自鸣钟，并指导宫中匠人制造钟表。后由于宫内制造的钟表远远满足不了帝后和达官显贵的需求，因此，皇帝不惜重金购买外国的钟表。从清宫的《活计档》、《贡单》档案中可以看到，仅乾隆年间粤海关购买及各地方官员进贡的钟表大约有2700余件，其中大量是英国的。

英国是世界上制造机械钟表较早的国家之一。1348年在伦敦出现了第一座自鸣钟。早期的英制机械时钟是利用调节重锤的摆动以控制擒纵机构的，体积庞大，多安装在公共场所和教堂等高大建筑上。14世纪至16世纪伦敦出现了长箱钟和桌钟，其中托马斯·汤姆皮恩和丹尼尔·夸尔等人所制堪称佳品。他们制作的长箱摆钟表面有刻花和镂空花纹，金属板上也錾花为饰。托马斯·汤姆皮恩为英国威廉三世（1689－1702年在位）的汉普顿宫卧室制造的钟可连续走三个月。丹尼尔·夸尔为英国白金汉宫制造的木匣钟能连续走十二个月，可惜这些钟都没能保存下来。

18世纪英国伦敦有几十家钟表工厂，其中在钟表上署名的有威廉森（Williamson）、詹姆斯·考克斯（James Cox）、乔治·希金森（George Higginson）、威廉·卡本特（William Carpenter）、约翰·保罗（John Barrow）、威廉·休斯（William Hughes）、本杰明·沃德（Benjamin Ward）等，还有许多没有署名的钟表，制作得也非常精致，可以和前者媲美。

英国伦敦的威廉森氏是有名的钟表世家。约瑟夫·威廉森（Joseph Williamson）是英国安妮女王时期（1702-1714年）的钟表匠师，他发明了走时准确的天文钟和标明日期、星期的日历钟，一生工作勤奋，最后死在工作室里。他的后代提摩泰·威廉森（Timothy Williamson）制作的钟表形式多样，有精确的走时、报时、奏乐的机械，还有连动的人物装置等，如铜镀金写字人钟，为四层楼阁式，上边有两人，展示"万寿无疆"横幅；其下还有敲钟碗的人可打动；下层有一身穿绅士服装的欧洲人，当钟表启动后，他可以伏案书写"八方向化，九土来王"八个字。是一件机械结构十分复杂的钟，是专为宫廷制作的。

詹姆斯·考克斯（James Cox）大约于1760－1765年间曾运用大气压力，制造了一座大瓶装置的气压钟，使弦的松紧通过气压升降来调整，可以自动走时三个月。他制造的各式各样造型优美，走时准确的钟，大约于1772年在伦敦的考克斯博物馆里展出过。1783－1790年考克斯父子还在中国广东设立钟表公司，设计出多种具有中国风格的座钟，如铜镀金四方形跳杆鸟音笼表，是他的代表作。满族贵族都有提笼遛鸟的嗜好，此表启动后小鸟来回跳跃十分可爱，既是取悦帝后的艺术品，又是计时用具。考克斯于1788年去世，之后他的儿子继续经营这个公司，直到1792年。

英国钟表制作分工非常精细，其外型多采用铜镀金的框架，式样为欧洲古典建筑式、教堂式、宝塔式，以及各种动物造型，表面装饰多用玻璃、料石、珐琅等材料，色彩艳丽。内部结构都装有走时、报时、奏乐等，在计时的同时还充分利用发条为动源的齿轮联动系统，安装了一些活动的人物、鸟兽造型和水法等。小的怀表也十分精美，有的还嵌有珍贵的红蓝宝石和钻石。

北京故宫博物院所藏的英国钟表不仅是宫中的计时用具，也是宫中重要的陈设品和艺术佳品，如今即使在英国也难以见到这些绝妙的钟表。它们成为了解和研究英国钟表制造发展史非常宝贵的实物资料。

法国钟表 法国是制造机械钟表较早的国家之一。14世纪，在法国巴黎的公共场所出现了大众报时钟。自1396年法国出现了冠轮擒纵机构以后，西欧的制钟业有了很大发展。1459年法国的钟表匠曾为查理七世国王制成了第一架弹簧钟（即发条钟）。15世纪末到16世纪初，在意大利、法国和德国相继试制出蛋形表，以及各种式样的塔钟和四面钟等。17世纪法国制成了摆钟，不少法国的钟表匠师对于钟的发条、游丝、擒纵机构进行了精心研究和制造，对于机械钟表的发展起到了积极的推动作用。法国资产阶级革命以后，生产钟表的行业广泛运用机械生产，钟表在满足本国需要的同时，出口到东方，北京故宫博物院收藏的法国钟表，大部分是19世纪末到20世纪初的产品。

法国钟表的外壳多为金属结构，表面装饰以掐丝珐琅、画珐琅、料石镶嵌等工艺为主，色调典雅，其样式有仿教堂建筑式、围屏式、奖杯式、轮船式、火车头式、鸟笼式等，其内部结构变化较多，有以坠砣为动力的"滚钟"，以钢球为动力的"压力钟"等，有的钟表上还装有"寒暑表"、"风雨表"、"八音琴"、"指南针"等仪器。故宫博物院所藏法国钟表有的是巴黎制造的，有的是法国人在中国开设的钟表公司制造的。

瑞士钟表 瑞士也是制造机械钟表较早的国家之一。瑞士的钟表业与意大利、法国的钟表业有着千丝万缕的关系。16世纪中叶，日内瓦成为生产摆钟的重要产地，这里除了本地匠人以外还有移居到日内瓦的意大利、法国的制表人。大约于1700年，日内瓦钟表匠第一次用有孔的红宝石做为滑动的轴承，从此开始了用宝石安装在手表内做为轴承。1786年生产了自动上弦的表，此表秒针每经过一秒跳动一次，这只怀表是以后手表的雏形。四年后在瑞士日内瓦制成了世界上第一只手表。瑞士钟表逐渐完善，并向小型化发展。至19世纪时，瑞士钟表华丽精致，机芯精细，在世界上享有盛名。

瑞士的怀表薄而小，用黄金、银或铜镀金做壳，装饰绚丽多彩，有的镶嵌钻石、珍珠，以及精致的珐琅画；有的雕有多彩的花卉、禽鸟、人物等，形象逼真。其造型别致，除圆形表外，还有扇面形、锁形、昆虫形等。北京故宫博物院收藏的瑞士钟表大部分是19世纪、20世纪初的产品。其中有播威（Bovet，1820－1918年）、有威（Juvet，1848－1891年）、利威（Levy，1880－1900）、乌利文（Ullmann，1893－20世纪初）等人的制品。

除此以外，北京故宫博物院还收藏着少量的意大利、丹麦、日本、美国等的钟表，其做工也十分精细，造型别致，是这些国家钟表中的上品。

Contents

1. Clocks Made in China

Clocks Made in the Forbidden City Workshop, Qing Dynasty

Clocks Made in Guangzhou

Clocks Made in Suzhou

II. European Clocks and Watches

British Clocks and Watches

目 录

一、中国钟表

1

Sandalwood Pavilion Chiming Clock

Qianlong period
(1736-95)
Clock Workshop,
Forbidden City
103 x 50 x 41.5cm

紫檀木亭式时刻更钟
清乾隆年间
(1736 – 1795 年)
清宫造办处制
103 × 50 × 41.5厘米

Clocks Made in the Forbidden City Workshop, Qing Dynasty 清 宫 造 办 处 制 造

Carved on sandalwood, the clock carries the words "Made in the Qianlong Period" and has five keyholes for winding. Its functions include announcing every quarter of an hour, every hour and every watch (one of the five two-hour periods the night was divided into). At the back there are dials for adjusting the night watches and seasonal divisions. The copper mechanism in the square pavilion at the top part of the clock strikes the hours and night watches.

整体用紫檀木雕成，钟盘上有"乾隆年制"四字并有五个上弦眼。此钟的功能包括走时、报时、报刻、发更、打更。钟后有调打更数和调节气的盘。报时、打更时，顶部方亭内的铜件敲击发出声响。

2
Sandalwood, Double-eaved Tower Striking Clock

Qianlong period
(1736-1795)
Clock Workshop,
Forbidden City
152 x 70 x 70cm

紫檀重檐楼阁式更钟
清乾隆年间
(1736 – 1795 年)
清宫造办处制
152 × 70 × 70 厘米

清 宫 造 办 处 制 造 *Clocks Made in the Forbidden City Workshop. Zing Dynasty*

The clock takes the shape of an ancient tower with double eaves. The sandalwood frame is inlaid with jade carved with a stylized dragon and cloud design and enameled bats. It is a representative work of the early clocks made in the Forbidden City.

The clock strikes the quarters, hours and night watches. On the dial are two smaller dials, the left one for telling the night watches and the right one for telling the 24 lunar terms of the year. The sounds it strikes at the quarters, hours and watches vary in pitch so as to mark the different times.

　　钟的整体造型为古代重檐楼阁式。紫檀木钟壳上装饰夔龙纹玉雕片、云纹和蝙蝠图案的珐琅片。该钟是清宫做钟处早期代表性产品。

　　钟的功能有走时、报时、报刻、夜间打更。钟盘上方有两个小圆盘，左边为定更盘，右边为显示二十四节气的节气盘。报时、打刻、打更声，或清脆，或沉厚，以便区分。

31

3

Black Lacquer and Painted Tower Clock Decorated with Eight Immortals Presenting Birthday Gifts

14th year of the Qianlong period (1749) Clock Workshop, Forbidden City 185 x 102 x 70cm

黑漆彩绘楼阁群仙祝寿钟
清乾隆十四年(1749年)
清宫造办处制
185 × 102 × 70厘米

清 宫 造 办 处 制 造 *Clocks Made in the Forbidden City Workshop, Qing Dynasty*

This clock sits on a rectangular table, also decorated with black lacquer and with painted patterns to form a harmonious whole.

The center of the lower part of the tower is made of white porcelain and yellow enamel, with four characters meaning "Made in the Qianlong Period". The mechanical system consists of seven springs. There are five winding keyholes on the dial for regulating five springs with the functions of showing and chiming the quarters and hours. The bottom part has two holes for regulating two springs which control the turning of the backdrop on both the left and right.

When fully wound, it strikes at 3, 6, 9 and 12 hours, when the three doors on the second level automatically open to reveal three figures holding hammers and bells. The left and right figures strike the bell to announce the quarters, and the one in the middle strikes the bell to mark the hour. Then all three retreat into the tower. Music then plays, and the backdrops on both sides begin to move. On the left, the crane and the immortal dance, the sea surges and a pavilion gradually rises. On the right, between the hills of Fairyland, a figure is shown enjoying his birthday party, accepting gifts presented by the Eight Immortals. At the bottom part two are gilt buttons for controlling the turning of the decorations inside the tower.

According to the archives, the Clock Workshop received a blueprint for this clock from a European designer in 1743, and completed it in 1749.

木质黑漆彩绘楼阁式钟，钟座为一黑漆彩绘长方桌，与钟身浑然一体。

钟盘在楼阁底部正中，为白磁黄珐琅质，上有"乾隆年制"四字。钟内运转系统由七盘发条组成，钟盘有五个上弦孔，控制五盘发条，功能为走时、报刻、报时、发起、发打。钟底座上有二弦孔，控制二盘发条，带动楼阁底部左右布景的转动。

钟有多种功能，上弦走时后，逢三、六、九、十二时，机器发动，二层三扇楼门自动打开，走出三个手持钟锤、钟碗的小人。左右两人先击钟碗报刻，而后中间一人敲打钟碗报时，钟声止，三人退回楼阁门内。乐起，钟盘两侧布景开始活动：左侧仙鹤，仙人翔舞，海水滚动，一楼阁冉冉升起；右侧在仙山之间，有一寿星接受八仙献宝。楼阁底座有二个铜镀金旋钮，控制楼阁内景物的运转。

根据档案记载，此钟为乾隆八年(1743年)造办处欧洲技师画样，由清宫做钟处制作，于乾隆十四年(1749年)完成。

清宫造办处制造 *Clocks Made in the Forbidden City Workshop, Qing Dynasty*

4
Black Lacquer, Gilded Tower Clock

*Qianlong period
(1736-1795)
Clock Workshop,
Forbidden City
79 x 49 x 49cm*

黑漆描金楼式钟
清乾隆年间
(1736 — 1795 年)
清宫造办处制
79 × 49 × 49厘米

Clocks Made in the Forbidden City Workshop, Qing Dynasty 清宫造办处制造

The shape of the frame and the exterior decorations resemble those of traditional Chinese temple architecture. The dial is rendered in light enamel patterns, with four characters meaning "Made in the Qianlong Period". It strikes the quarters, hours and night watches. The two top holes are used for adjusting the night watches and the 24 lunar terms, respectively. The two semicircles below reveal the mechanical structure. When a night watch is struck, the gear activates a cylinder, which in turn activates the hammer to strike the bell, producing a crisp sound.

钟壳造型及外饰髹漆均仿制寺庙建筑与工艺,整体色泽古朴浓厚。钟盘配以淡彩珐琅花纹,上有"乾隆年制"四字,能走时、打时、打刻、发更、打更。上部有二小孔用于调更和调节气,小孔下方半圆形洞,露出内部机械结构。打更时,由齿轮带动带刺滚筒,拨动钟锤,敲打钟碗,发出洪亮的打更声响。

5
Double-eaved Tower Clock Decorated with Revolving Eight Immortals

Qianlong period (1736-1795) Clock Workshop, Forbidden City 86 x 50 x 40cm

重檐楼阁式转八仙钟
清乾隆年间
(1736 — 1795 年)
清宫造办处制造
86 × 50 × 40 厘米

清 宫 造 办 处 制 造 *Clocks Made in the Forbidden City Workshop. Qing Dynasty*

The clock has three sets of springs and strikes the quarters, hours and night watches. Behind the tower is a winding hole, and when the clock is fully wound, the Eight Immortals in the pavilion start revolving. The Eight Immortals are eight mythical figures of the Taoist tradition, namely Han Zhongli, Lu Dongbin, Zhang Guolao, Han Xiangzi, Cripple Li, Emperor's Cousin Cao, Lan Caihe and Fairy Lady He. These eight figures are a common feature of Qing Dynasty clocks.

钟体内有三盘发条，能走时、报时。楼阁后有弦孔，上弦后可带动阁内的八仙像围树石转动。八仙是中国民间传说中的八位道家仙人，即汉钟离、吕洞宾、张果老、韩湘子、铁拐李、曹国舅、蓝采和、何仙姑。清代钟表中以八仙为装饰的屡屡可见。

6
Clock on a Chest Held by Two Boys

*Qianlong period
(1736-1795)
Clock Workshop,
Forbidden City
85.5 x 60 x 30cm*

双童托柜表
清乾隆年间
(1736 – 1795年)
清宫造办处制
85.5 × 60 × 30厘米

Clocks Made in the Forbidden City Workshop, Zing Dynasty 清宫造办处制造

The designer cleverly combined the clock, a storage chest and a lacquer painting into a harmonious whole. The two boys, with bodies made of copper and heads made of ivory, support a glass-covered chest the doors of which are lacquered. On the left edge of the chest is a button for opening it. The chest is divided into a series of pigeon holes for the safe-keeping of antiques. A clock with two hands is fixed to the top of the chest. The back of the clock carries the English inscription "Geo. Beefield London," indicating that the clock was made in Britain, although the frame was produced in the Forbidden City. Hence here is a product combining Chinese and Western technology.

　　设计者巧妙地将钟表、贮物柜与供欣赏的漆画集于一体。两端的托柜童子为铜身，头部用象牙雕成。柜门为一幅漆画，上罩有玻璃，柜左边沿有一门钮，柜内有大小不同的格子，可存贮珍玩宝物。二针表安装柜顶端，表板后刻有"Geo Beefield London"英文字样，可知此表为英国制造，表壳为清宫造办处制，是中西合璧的产物。

7

**Gilded Copper
Hand-rest Clock**

*Qianlong period
(1736-1795)
Clock Workshop,
Forbidden City
30 x 32 x 32cm*

铜镀金迎手钟
清乾隆年间
(1736 – 1795 年)
清宫造办处制
30 × 32 × 32 厘米

清 宫 造 办 处 制 造 *Clocks Made in the Forbidden City Workshop, Qing Dynasty*

This clock receives its name from its resemblance to the armrests on the imperial throne. The gilded body and meticulously executed carvings give it an air of elegance and luxury. The top of the clock is covered with brocade. The front of the octagonal frame bears a clock face with two hands, while the other three sides are decorated with openwork carving of flower patterns.

The mechanical part includes a musical movement. The wheel activates an air bag, from which air pressure produces a whistling sound. Gently pressing the brocade cover activates the mechanism which produces the music.

此钟形似宫殿内宝座两边的迎手，即放手之物，故名。钟体金碧华贵，雕刻精细，与帝后宝座融为一体。上面为锦缎盖，八角形的钟壳正面嵌有二针时钟，其它三面嵌镂雕花卉。

钟内部有一套奏乐装置，机械带动齿轮，拨动充气袋，气流冲击哨子发出声响。轻压锦缎盖，即可触动机器，令乐声响起。

8
Gilded Copper Hat-rack Clock

*Qianlong period
(1736-1795)
Clock Workshop,
Forbidden City
48 x 20 x 9cm*

铜镀金冠架钟
清乾隆年间
(1736 – 1795年)
清宫造办处制
48 × 20 × 9厘米

Clocks Made in the Forbidden City Workshop, Zing Dynasty 清 宫 造 办 处 制 造

The frame is fully decorated with flower patterns gilded on copper and carries characters meaning "Made in the Qianlong Period". The dial has three winding holes, and its mechanical system consists of a spring, chain and cone pulley. It strikes the quarters and the hours. On top of the clock are three small spiral pillars for hanging hats on.

钟壳布满铜镀金卷草花纹饰，上部有"乾隆年制"字样。钟盘上有三个弦孔，内部结构以发条、链条、塔轮组成，功能有走时、打时、打刻。钟顶有三个螺旋式的柱子可放帽子，称为"冠架"，钟由此得名。

9
Gilded Tower Clock

*Qianlong period
(1736-1795)
Clock Workshop,
Forbidden City
36 x 22.7 x 16cm*

金漆楼阁式钟
清乾隆年间
(1736 – 1795 年)
清宫造办处制
36 × 22.7 × 16厘米

清 宫 造 办 处 制 造 *Clocks Made in the Forbidden City Workshop, Qing Dynasty*

This clock is characterized by smooth outlines. The lacquer surface is rendered with hexagonal and cloud patterns. The lower part resembles an upside-down bowl. Diamond-shaped patterns cover the clock stand. On the top part of the dial are characters meaning "Made in the Qianlong Period". It strikes both the quarters and the hours.

钟体外形线条简洁流畅，髹金漆上绘六角形和云纹纹饰。下部像一个倒扣的钟碗，棱形纹装饰底座四周。盘面上方有"乾隆年制"四字，有三孔为上弦处，分别走时、打时和打刻。

10
Alarm Clock

Qianlong Period
(1736-1795)
Clock Workshop,
Forbidden City
12.5cm (diameter),
7.5 cm (thick)

时辰醒钟
清乾隆年间
(1736 – 1795 年)
清宫造办处制
直径12.5厘米
厚7.5厘米

Clocks Made in the Forbidden City Workshop, Qing Dynasty 清 宫 造 办 处 制 造

This round brass clock has a simple and smooth appearance. On its back are two winding holes, one for adjusting the time and the other for setting the alarm. The center of the dial contains two smaller discs. The outer disc is of white porcelain and bears the characters for the 12 traditional divisions of the day.

醒钟即为闹钟。钟为紫铜圆形，制作简洁明快。钟背面有两孔，一孔走时，一孔专拨"闹"时。钟盘中心有二个圆铜盘，其外圈是白磁盘，上用楷体书写子、丑、寅、卯、辰、巳、午、未、申、酉、戌、亥十二时辰，作为计时数字。这种古代的计时制，每一时辰为两个小时。时针指向"子"为半夜12时，子时即由晚11时至凌晨1时；时针指向"午"为白天正午12时，午时由上午11时至下午1时。时针转一周为二十四小时。

11

Gilded Clock Decorated with Revolving Eight Immortals, Fountain and Flowers

Qianlong period (1736-1795)
Clock Workshop, Forbidden City
84 x 35 x 24cm

铜镀金八仙水法转花钟
清乾隆年间
(1736 – 1795年)
清宫造办处制造
84 × 35 × 24 厘米

清宫造办处制造 *Clocks Made in the Forbidden City Workshop, Qing Dynasty*

The stand of the clock is a musical box, the front part of which is decorated with a landscape painting. Spiral legs at the four corners of the clock stand support the oblong clock frame, which is decorated with a painting in colored enamel. In the central part of the frame is a double-hand dial. At the back of the frame is a mirror. A revolving plate decorated with the sculptured images of the Eight Immortals is located next to the axle under the clock frame. On the two sides are pagoda revolving flowers. When the clock is activated, the figures and boat in the landscape painting move, and the Eight Immortals and flowers revolve.

此钟底座为乐箱，正面为一风景画。底座上方四角曲腿支架支撑着椭圆形钟壳，钟壳正面为色彩艳丽的珐琅画，中间有一两针小表。钟壳背面嵌一镜子。钟壳下中心圆轴旁有转盘，上有八仙塑像，两侧还有塔式转花。启动后，风景画中人物，船只行走，八仙像和塔式转花转动。

12
Wood-and-Plaster
Bird Cage Clock

Clock Workshop,
Forbidden City
57 x 39 x 25cm

木制泥金鸟笼式表
清宫造办处制
57 × 39 × 25厘米

Clocks Made in the Forbidden City Workshop. Zing Dynasty 清 宫 造 办 处 制 造

The stand is made of wood rendered with flower patterns done on plaster and painted in gold. In the center of the stand is a white enamel dial. Inside the stand, a mechanical system activates the clock and a musical box

On the left of the gilded copper bird cage is a movable opening with two winding holes. When fully wound, the flower in the cage revolves, and the four birds sing.

底座用木料做成，上贴石膏制作的卷草花纹饰，并涂抹金粉。底座正中嵌有白珐琅表盘，底座内的机芯由一组带动表盘转动的机械结构和乐箱两部分组成。

铜镀金鸟笼罩的左侧有一个可以活动的门，门下方有两孔，上弦后，笼中的花卉旋转，四只鸟儿摇摆鸣叫。

13
Double-sided Mahogany Clock

Qianlong period (1736-1795)
Clock Workshop, Forbidden City
58cm in diameter

红木座双面钟
清乾隆年间
(1736 – 1795 年)
清宫造办处制
直径 58 厘米

清 宫 造 办 处 制 造 *Clocks Made in the Forbidden City Workshop, Qing Dynasty*

The stand and dial rest are made of mahogany carved with cloud, mountain and sea patterns. The central part of the dial is decorated with gilded copper flowers which are encircled by a copper ring on which the 24 hours are indicated. An outer copper ring indicates the 60 minutes of the hour. On both sides of the clock, there is a dial and two hands. Inside the clock, a spring, a cone pulley and a chain activate the hands.

　　钟座和钟盘支架用红木雕刻成流云、山、海形状。钟盘中心装饰铜镀金缠枝花，花卉周边有一道铜圈，上面刻有二十四个格，时针走一圈为二十四小时。钟盘上有十二个嵌螺钿的罗马数字，代表十二时辰。最外一道铜圈刻有 60 个格，每格一分钟，分针转一圈为一小时。钟的前后均有钟盘和二指针。钟内由一组发条盒、塔轮、链条为动源，带动两面钟同时运行。

14
Blossoming Flower Clock

*Qianlong period
(1736-1795)
Clock Workshop,
Forbidden City
118cm high, 49cm in
diameter*

自开花献桃荷花缸钟
清乾隆年间
(1736 – 1795 年)
清宫造办处制
高 118 厘米
缸直径 49 厘米

Clocks Made in the Forbidden City Workshop, Qing Dynasty 清 宫 造 办 处 制 造

The vat-shaped clock frame is decorated with threaded enamel patterns of butter-flies and flowers. On the vat are red lotuses in full or half blossom. On three of the flowers sit the Queen Mother of the West, a fairy boy and a white ape, respectively, as symbols of good luck, which are all figures in Chinese fairytales. A glass mirror in the vat symbolizes a water surface, and on it sit eight Mandarin ducks. On the side of the vat is a three-hand dial 12 centimeters in diameter. The dial plate has two holes, with the left one for adjusting the time and the right one for controlling the music and the movement of the ornaments in the vat. The mechanical part is hidden inside the vat. When activated, the lotus flowers open up amidst music to reveal the Queen Mother of the West, the fairy boy and the white ape. The flower petals close upon them when the music stops. The clock was made for Emperor Qianlong's birthday. The vat was made by the palace's enamel workshop, while the clock was produced by the clock workshop.

缸式的钟壳通体为掐丝珐琅彩蝶花卉图案；缸上是盛开或半开的红色荷花，其中有三朵荷花中分别坐有神话故事中的女神西王母、仙童和象征吉祥的白猿。缸中铺玻璃镜充作水面，上置有八只鸳鸯。缸的旁侧安装直径约 12 厘米的三针时钟，钟盘上有二孔，左边控制走时，右边控制乐曲和缸中的装饰物。机械暗藏于缸内，启动后伴着乐声，荷花张开，露出端坐花中的王母、仙童和捧蟠桃的白猿，乐止瓣合。此钟为皇帝祝寿而作，缸由清宫珐琅作坊制造，时钟和内部机械均由做钟处制作安装。

清宫造办处制造 *Clocks Made in the Forbidden City Workshop. Qing Dynasty*

15
Revolving Wooden Pagoda Clock

Qianlong period
(1736-1795)
Clock Workshop,
Forbidden City
145 x 52 x 52cm

木质塔式转八仙乐钟
清乾隆年间
(1736 – 1795 年)
清宫造办处制
145 × 52 × 52 厘米

Clocks Made in the Forbidden City Workshop, Qing Dynasty 清宫造办处制造

The dial plate is inlaid in the front part of the base of a hexagonal pagoda. The clock has two hands and strikes every hour.

The wooden pagoda consists of 13 stories, and the pillars of the base are made of jade. The heart of the pagoda is a round pillar, and the eaves boast meticulously executed elegant carvings. On each story under the eaves are eight immortal figures, making up a total of 104, all holding different kinds of treasures in their hands. A spring at the back of the pagoda base makes the pillar revolve, with the odd-numbered and even-numbered stories turning in opposite directions.

钟盘嵌于六角形塔基的正面，为二针钟，可走时、报时。
木塔模型共十三层，底层围以青玉栏杆。塔中心为一圆柱，塔檐雕刻精美，每层檐内走廊上塑有8个仙人，全塔共104个，手持不同宝物。转动塔基后的发条可带动圆柱转动，单、双数塔层分别依顺、逆时针方向转动。

16
Copper Flower-inlaid Tower Clock

*Qianlong period
(1736-1795)
Clock Workshop,
Forbidden City
64 x 35.3 x 13cm*

木楼嵌铜花钟
清乾隆年间
（1736 — 1795 年）
清宫造办处制
64 × 35.3 × 13 厘米

清 宫 造 办 处 制 造 *Clocks Made in the Forbidden City Workshop, Qing Dynasty*

The frame of the clock resembles a European building, but the gilded copper decorative patterns inlaid on the frame combine both European and Chinese artistic styles. The dial has three winding holes, and the clock strikes both the quarters and the hours.

钟壳造型仿欧洲建筑形式，钟壳上嵌贴的铜镀金纹饰兼具欧洲与中国工艺的风格。钟盘有三个上弦孔，可走时、报时、打刻。

17

Sandalwood Screen Clock

Qianlong period (1736-1795)
Clock Workshop, Forbidden City
35.2 x 30 x 13cm

紫檀插屏钟
清乾隆年间
(1736 — 1795 年)
清宫造办处制
35.2 × 30 × 13厘米

Clocks Made in the Forbidden City Workshop. Qing Dynasty 清 宫 造 办 处 制 造

The edge of the sandalwood frame is carved with stylized dragon patterns. An opening in the upper part of the dial reveals a pendulum. The dial surface has three keyholes for winding and activating the mechanical parts. The dial is marked in both minutes and hours. It strikes every hour.

　紫檀木外壳周边雕有夔龙纹饰。夔龙原是中国传说中一种形状近似龙的动物,中国古代器物常用它的形象作装饰。钟盘上部有横缺口,露出明摆。盘面有三孔,用以上弦、发动机械。钟盘上标有计分、计时数字。可以走分、走刻、打时。

18
Fanning Figure Clock

Qianlong period (1736-1795)
Clock Workshop, Forbidden City
96 x 44 x 40cm

搧扇机器人钟
清乾隆年间
(1736 – 1795 年)
清宫造办处制造
96 × 44 × 40 厘米

清 宫 造 办 处 制 造 *Clocks Made in the Forbidden City Workshop, Qing Dynasty*

The stand, made of gilded copper, has a figure and a landscape painting on each of the four sides. The paintings are framed in blue enamel. On the left part of the rectangular stand sits an image of a palace maid. When the mechanical part is activated, she waves a fan up and down, while her head turns left and right. On the right side of the stand is a copper elephant which carries on its back a double-hand clock which strikes every hour.

铜镀金框钟座，台座四面中嵌有四幅山水人物风景画，画框外饰蓝地珐琅，方形台座左侧置一宫廷仕女坐像，机械启动后，持扇手臂上下摇动，同时头左右摆动。台座右侧立一铜象，背负二指针钟，有走时、报时功能。

19
Yuan Dynasty Water Clock

Guangzhou Museum
264.4cm high

元延祐三年(1316年)
漏壶
广州博物馆藏
通高264.4厘米

Clocks Made in the Forbidden City Workshop, Qing Dynasty 清 宫 造 办 处 制 造

    This clock consists of four containers, respectively named the sun-, moon-, star- and water-receiving containers, placed on a staircase frame. The containers have spouts at the bottom carved in the shape of a dragon's head to let the water leak out at a calculated rate. The water-receiving container has a copper ruler marked with the 12 traditional divisions of the day. Pointing to the respective markings on the ruler is a wooden arrow connected to a floating boat in the container.

    At 5:15 every morning and 17:15 in the late afternoon, the sun container is refilled with water, which drips through the dragon head into the next container, and finally into the water-receiving container. The accumulation of water pushes up the floating boat, which in turn makes the arrow rise.

    漏壶由四个铜壶组成, 日壶、月壶、星壶、受水壶, 自上而下依次摆放在阶梯式座架上, 四壶均有盖。日壶、月壶、星壶底处有龙头滴水。受水壶盖中央插一把铜尺, 自上至下刻有十二时辰, 铜尺前插入一支木制的浮箭, 与壶内浮舟相连。

    每日早晨5:15时, 下午17:15时, 各向日壶注一次水, 日壶内的水经龙口依次流入下壶, 最后滴进受水壶。受水壶内浮舟漂起, 浮箭不断升出受水壶盖, 从铜尺上所刻的时辰观察计时。

20
***Sandalwood Tower
Chiming Clock***

*Qianlong period
(1736-1795)
Clock Workshop,
 Forbidden City
585 x 262 x 262cm*

紫檀木雕楼式自鸣钟
清乾隆年间
(1736 – 1795 年)
清宫造办处制
585 × 262 × 262 厘米

清 宫 造 办 处 制 造 *Clocks Made in the Forbidden City Workshop, Qing Dynasty*

The carved sandalwood clock frame is in the shape of a square pavilion with two stories. The dial plate is inlaid in the panel of the upper story, with a gilded flower pattern surface. On the top of the pavilion are two upside-down brass bells. On the side of the bells is a hammer the handle of which is connected to the mechanical part of the clock. Every quarter and hour, the mechanical part pulls the handle of the hammer, which strikes the upper bell once for every quarter. After the bell has been sounded four times, the hammer strikes the lower bell to announce the hour. The number of strikes matches the actual hour. The clock is wound from behind, and once fully wound it can keep working for three days and three nights.

The clock is activated by three sets of inter-connected mechanical parts for striking the quarter, striking the hour and moving to keep the time. It is the largest chime clock made in the Clock Workshop during the Qianlong period now preserved in the Palace Museum.

钟外壳为紫檀雕花方形楼阁式，分上下两层。钟盘嵌在上层铜镀金錾花板面上。楼阁上方倒扣两铜钟，钟旁各有一锤，每个锤柄一端与钟机相连，每逢报时、刻时，钟机牵动钟柄，钟柄带动钟锤击钟。敲打上边铜钟，报一刻敲一响，以此类推，四刻四响完后，敲打下边的铜钟报时，几时几响。上弦处，在钟背后门里，每上一次弦，可以走三昼夜。

紫檀木雕楼式自鸣钟，是由控制报刻、报时和走时的三组机械结构相互联动，以带动钟的运转。由于它能按时报时刻，称为自鸣钟。它是宫中现存乾隆时期清宫造办处造制的最大一座自鸣钟。

21
Copper Water Clock in the Hall of Celestial and Terrestrial Union

9th year of the Qianlong period (1744)
Clock Workshop, Forbidden City

交泰殿铜壶滴漏
清乾隆九年(1744年)
清宫造办处制

Clocks Made in the Forbidden City Workshop, Qing Dynasty 清 宫 造 办 处 制 造

This water clock is kept in a sandalwood double-eaved pavilion in the eastern section of the Hall of Celestial and Terrestrial Union in the Palace Museum. The pavilion is 588.8cm high. It bears an inscription by Emperor Qianlong.

The water clock is made up of five brass containers. The top three, namely, the day, night and level containers are square in shape and are collectively known as the "water giving containers". Behind the level container is one for regulating the speed of the water flow. The lowest container, in a round shape, is called the "water-receiving container". In its middle is a brass figure sitting cross-legged on a lotus flower and holding a brass ruler marked with the 12 traditional divisions of the day. The ruler is connected to a float in the container.

At 11:00 in the morning, the top container is filled with water, which begins to flow from the dragon's mouth in the front to the next container. In the same fashion, the water finally flows into the lowest container. The rising water in this container pushes up the float, which raises the ruler. The speed of the water flow exactly matches the movement of the sun. After 24 hours, the water-receiving container is filled up.

漏壶位于故宫交泰殿内东侧，置于紫檀木重檐楼阁内，楼阁通高588.8厘米。壶上镌刻有乾隆帝的《刻漏铭》。

交泰殿漏壶由五个铜壶组成，由上至下排列着日天壶、夜天壶、平水壶三个方斗形铜壶，称为"播水壶"，平水壶后侧有一个分水壶，用来调节水的速度。最下方的圆形铜壶，称为"受水壶"。受水壶，壶盖中心有一铜人盘腿坐在莲花座上，双手合抱一把刻有十二时辰的漏箭(即铜尺)下端插入受水壶内与壶中鼓形箭舟(即水漂)相连。

每日正午11时，从最上面的日天壶注满水，水从壶前龙口流出，依次向下壶滴漏，至最底的受水壶，受水壶水位上涨，箭舟(水漂)浮起，托着漏箭(铜尺)上升，水流速度恰合于太阳移动速度。经过一昼夜的滴漏，受水壶水满箭尽露出水面，将水泻入受水壶下面的铜池内，再重新装水滴漏。

22
Sundial in Front of the Hall of Supreme Harmony

74cm in diameter, 8cm in thickness

太和殿日晷

直径74厘米　厚8厘米

Clocks Made in the Forbidden City Workshop. Qing Dynasty 清 宫 造 办 处 制 造

The face of the sundial on the terrace in front of the Hall of Supreme Harmony in the Forbidden City slants at a 39.55-degree angle, so as to be parallel with the equator; hence it is known as an equator-type sundial.

The dial plate is marked on both sides with lines indicating the directions of the compass, and the time division units are marked with Chinese characters. These markings, however, have been eroded over the centuries.

太和殿日晷，位于太和殿前，是宫中计时器。石制的圆形晷盘向北倾斜，夹角为39度55分，与地球赤道相平行，又称赤道式日晷。

铁质晷针从晷盘中心穿过，上下长短相等，随着太阳每日自东向西移动和一年中直射点南北移动，晷针投射在晷盘上的影子的方向位置也随之变化。

晷盘两面均刻有表示方向和时辰的刻度线并标有代表方位、时辰的汉字。

由于日晷长年在外风吹日晒已经风化，晷盘上面的刻线和字迹已模糊不清。

23
Gilded Copper and Enamel-inlaid Clock Decorated with Tree and Fairy

Qianlong period (1736-1795)
Made in Guangzhou
71 x 29 x 26cm

铜镀金嵌珐琅开花仙人钟
清乾隆年间
(1736 – 1795 年)
广州制造
71 × 29 × 26 厘米

广 州 制 造 *Clocks Made in Guangzhou*

This double-hand clock is inlaid in a flower pot made of purple enamel. Its dial is of white enamel. The flower pot has an artificial tree with a flower at the top that can open and close. On the flower sits a fairy. The lower part of the clock is a musical box in the front of which there is a fountain and a miniature bridge over a river. A man is rowing a boat on the river.

钟嵌于紫色珐琅花盆正面，为白珐琅二针表盘。花盆内装饰着人造花树，顶端大花朵可开可合，花中坐一仙女雕像。底层是乐箱，正面有水法装置，配有微缩的小桥流水、行人舟楫。

24
Four-sided Gilded Copper and Yellow Enamel Clock

Qianlong period
(1736-1795)
Made in Guangzhou
111 x 47 x 47cm

铜镀金嵌黄珐琅四面钟
清乾隆年间
(1736 – 1795 年)
广州制造
111 × 47 × 47 厘米

Clocks Made in Guangzhou 广 州 制 造

The four corner pillars of the frame are decorated with gilded copper dragon patterns. The frame bears yellow enamel flower patterns. The top resembles an umbrella, and is also made of enamel. There is a dial plate on each of the four sides. The second, minute and hour hands are activated by a set of springs, chains and cone pulleys. An arch gate above the dial houses a sculptured figure in an official's red robe. When it strikes the hour, the official makes an appearance, and the three sets of couplets on the sides of the gate change in sequence. They respectively mean "A peaceful world in a harmonious time, a good harvest and long-living people", "Favorable climate and fertile land, abundant resources and outstanding talents" and "Fine customs and good traditions, a joyful country and happy families". The clock strikes the hour to musical accompaniment.

框架四条棱上饰铜镀金龙纹。钟壳镶布满花卉纹的黄珐琅，顶部似伞盖，亦用珐琅烧制。四面都有钟盘，内装置一组发条、链条、塔轮，带动四面的时、分、秒针运行。钟盘上方有一拱门，内有红衣官人塑像。正点时，铃声起，官人出现，门两侧三副对联递相变换，它们分别是："时和世泰，人寿年丰"，"物华天宝，人杰地灵"，"俗美风纯，国恩家庆"。钟有走时、报时、打乐功能。

广 州 制 造 *Clocks Made in Guangzhou*

25

Gilded Copper Pavil-
ion Clock Decorated
with Swimming
Ducks and Revolving
Figures

Qianlong period
(1736-1795)
Made in Guangzhou
110 x 48 x 39cm

铜镀金亭式跑鸭转人钟
清乾隆年间
(1736 – 1795 年)
广州制造
110 × 48 × 39 厘米

The body of the clock is of gilded copper, with elegant openwork flower patterns. Figures are seen inside and outside the pavilion. On top of the dial plate is a bridge spanning a river, with swimming ducks. When the mechanism is activated, music plays, and the figures outside the pavilion make a gesture of offering treasures, while the figures inside the pavilion revolve around it, and the ducks begin swimming in the river. The dial plate has three adjustment holes, and the clock strikes both the quarters and the hours. Below the dial plate is a copper plate on each of the left and right sides. The one on the left is for music, while the right one is marked with seven spaces, representing the days of the week.

　　钟身为铜镀金，通体镂刻精美花纹。上部是尖顶方形亭子，亭内外有雕塑的小人。白色的钟盘上方，有一组活动图景：跨河小桥和水上浮鸭。启动奏乐后，亭上小人作献宝状，亭外小人绕亭转动；水中鸭子游动。钟盘上有三弦孔，功能为走时、报时、打刻。钟盘左右下方有二个小铜盘；左下方为乐曲盘；右下方的铜盘周沿等分成七小格，指针移动一格为一天，转动一圈为一周。

26
Gilded Copper Pavilion Striking Clock

*Qianlong period
(1736-1795)
Made in Guangzhou
83 x 39 x 30cm*

铜镀金亭式人打钟
清乾隆年间
(1736 — 1795 年)
广州制造
83 × 39 × 30 厘米

Clocks Made in Guangzhou 广 州 制 造

The bottom and two sides of the gilded copper stand with carved flower patterns have a fountain installation, with boat and figures on the water. The dial plate in the middle section is of white enamel and has three hands. In the pavilion in the upper section is a kneeling figure, which strikes two bells on the hour. The fountain, the four corners of the tower, the roof of the pavilion and the flowers at the upper part of the dial plate all revolve.

钟的主色调为蓝色,铜镀金雕花基座的底层及两侧有水法装置,内有流水行船和人物等;中层的钟盘为三针白磁盘,上层亭中跪一人,面前置两钟碗。每当报时的时候,亭中的人物敲打钟碗,发出悦耳的音乐声;水法涌动似流水;钟楼四角、亭顶和钟盘上方的料石转花同时转动。

广 州 制 造 *Clocks Made in Guangzhou*

27
*Gilded Copper Tower
Clock with Birthday
Celebration
Decorations*

*Qianlong period
(1736-1795)
Made in Guangzhou
63 x 28 x 22cm*

铜镀金楼式献寿钟
清乾隆年间
(1736 – 1795 年)
广州制造
63 × 28 × 22 厘米

The clock strikes the hour and plays music. The lower part is a musical box. In the front part is a two-hand dial plate. Above it are two smaller dials, with the one on the left for turning the music on and off, and the one on the right for selecting the tunes. In the pavilion at the top are two figures, one holding a peach and the other pulling a lion. When the music starts, the one with the peach kneels down, and the lion shakes its head as a birthday greeting. The peach is supposed to be one grown by the Queen Mother of the West, bestowing immortality

钟能走时、报时、奏乐。底层为乐箱，箱中有机械装置。正面为二针钟盘，钟盘上方有两个小圆盘，右为乐曲曲盘，左为乐曲启止盘。上部亭内塑有二人，一人双手捧桃，一人牵狮，启动后乐响，捧桃人跪下，狮子摆头，以示献桃庆寿。中国神话传说人吃了天上女神西王母栽种的蟠桃，可以长生不老。所以，民间常用鲜桃或蒸制的桃形面点作为寿礼。

28

Gilded Copper Enamel-inlaid Clock with Birthday Celebration Decorations

Qianlong period (1736-1795)
Made in Guangzhou
100 x 40 x 32cm

铜镀金嵌珐琅三人献寿钟
清乾隆年间
(1736 - 1795 年)
广州制造
100 × 40 × 32 厘米

Clocks Made in Guangzhou　广　州　制　造

The frame is of gilded copper decorated with enamel. The four corners of the stand are supported by a gilded copper goat. The front part of the stand is in the form of a stage scene with three figures. The one in the middle holds a scroll with the character for "longevity" written on it, and the other two each hold a peach. On the middle level is a figure holding a hammer with which it strikes 12 bells of varying sizes and thickness. When struck, they produce different sounds. At the top part of the clock is a white enamel dial with three hands. The winding holes are at the back of the clock. Around the stand of the clock are 12 revolving ivory figures. When the mechanism is activated, all the movable parts revolve accompanied by music.

　　钟外壳为铜镀金嵌珐琅装饰，底座四角由铜镀金羊背负钟体。底座正面似舞台布景，内塑有三人，中间一人手持"万寿无疆"字联，左右二人手捧桃盘献寿。中层门内塑一人手持钟锤，面前排列着十二个大小不同、薄厚各异的钟碗，敲打时发出不同的音响。上层为钟体，白磁三针表盘，弦孔在钟盘后部。钟座周围有十二个转动的牙雕小人。启动后，一切可活动物随乐声而动转。

广　州　制　造　*Clocks Made in Guangzhou*

29
Gilded Copper
Enamel Gourd Clock
Qianlong period
(1736-1795)
Made in Guangzhou
84 x 41 x 32cm

铜镀金珐琅葫芦式钟
清乾隆年间
(1736 – 1795 年)
广州制造
84 × 41 × 32 厘米

The top part of the clock is a gourd-shaped bottle floating in the basin of a fountain. The lower part is an oblong stand with an automatic door in the middle, which opens when music starts, to reveal an image of the God of Longevity. A magic herb, crane, deer and immortal animals on the sides all move in time to the music. At the same time, the fountain revolves, producing an impression of surging waves.

钟的上部是葫芦式瓶，浮于圆形的平铺水法上，下部为一椭圆座基，中间有一个自开门，乐起，门开，出现象征长寿的寿星像，周围仿制的灵芝、鹤、鹿、仙兽等祥瑞之物，随乐转动，与此同时，水法流转，如波涛涌起，葫芦瓶似飘浮在水上。

30
Gilded Copper Clock with Gourd-shaped Top

Qianlong period (1736-1795)
Made in Guangzhou
86 x 35 x 30cm

铜镀金葫芦顶楼式钟
清乾隆年间
(1736－1795年)
广州制造
86 × 35 × 30厘米

Clocks Made in Guangzhou 广 州 制 造

This tower clock consists of three levels. The gilded copper top level takes the shape of a gourd with flowers. The front side of the lower part of the gourd is inlaid with a spiraling flower pattern done with precious stones. The middle level features a white enamel dial with three handles. The mechanical part consists of springs, a cone pulley and chains, which activate the clock to strike the hour and produce music. The lower level has three arched gates. Inside on the left and right, are fountains. The middle gate has two red doors which can open to reveal a set of painted ivory figures standing in a circle and holding treasures in their hands. When the music starts, the flowers in the vases revolve, and the two red doors open automatically. The ivory figures make the gesture of offering the precious objects and the fountains play.

　　楼式的钟体分三层，顶为铜镀金錾花葫芦形，葫芦腹部正面嵌有料石旋转花。钟盘在中层的正面，白珐琅钟盘，三指针。钟内部由一组发条盒、塔轮、链条机械组成，带动钟走时、打时、打乐。下层有三拱门，左右门内有水法，中间有两扇可开关的红门，门内有一组彩绘牙雕人，手捧各种宝物，围成一圈。乐起，上下瓶中花束一起转动，两扇红门自动打开，牙雕人绕转并作献宝状，左右水法如喷泉涌出。

31
Gilded Copper Enamel Vase Clock Decorated with a Fisherman, Woodcutter, Farmer and Scholar

55th year of the Qianlong period (1790) Made in Guangzhou 94 x 47 x 40cm

铜镀金珐琅楼渔樵耕读钟
清乾隆五十五年
(1790年)
广州制造
94 × 47 × 40 厘米

广 州 制 造 *Clocks Made in Guangzhou*

The clock is of gilded copper decorated with enamel on the edge of the frame. The four corners of the stand are supported by four gilded copper sheep. The gourd-shaped enamel vase carries the character meaning "longevity" on the top level and the characters meaning "great luck" in the belly of the lower level. The characters are rendered on the surface of two movable doors which reveal revolving figures. The middle section of the clock is where the dial plate is. The lower section shows a movable scene decorated with images of a fisherman, a woodcutter, a farmer and a scholar. These figures constitute a common theme in ancient China to describe an idyllic life.

钟为铜镀金嵌珐琅框架，底座四角由四只铜镀金羊背负。顶层为葫芦形的珐琅瓶，瓶上腹饰寿字，中腹写有"大吉"字样的两扇活动门，内有能转动的小人。中层为钟盘。底层正中有一组由渔翁、樵夫、农民、读书人组成的活动图景，这是中国古时表现田园生活常用的题材，称作"渔樵耕读图"。

32
Enamel Pavilion Chiming Clock Decorated with Three Apes Offering Gifts

Qianlong period
(1736-1795)
Made in Guangzhou
110 x 43 x 29cm

珐琅亭式三猿献宝乐钟
清乾隆年间
(1736 — 1795 年)
广州制造
110 × 43 × 29厘米

Clocks Made in Guangzhou 广 州 制 造

The body of the clock is dominated by green enamel, decorated with coiling flower patterns. The middle of the clock has a three-hand dial which has a movable picture of "Three Apes Offering Gifts". When the clock is activated, the theater curtain rises to the accompaniment of music. The apes offer the gifts and then return to where they were. When the music stops, the curtain falls.

钟体以绿色珐琅为主，上饰缠枝花纹；上部为蓝色珐琅六角亭。钟座正中是三针钟盘，钟盘下方矩形框内有三猿献宝活动图景。启动后，框前的帘上卷，乐声响起，三只雕刻的猿猴在机械的控制下，探身献宝，献宝后，退回原处，乐止，帘落下。

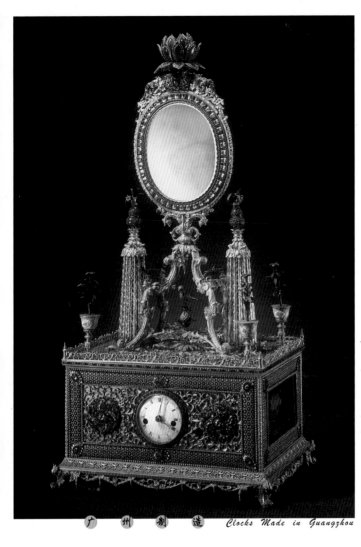

33
Gilded Copper Mirror Clock

Qianlong period (1736-1795)
Made in Guangzhou
59 x 30 x 23cm

铜镀金容镜钟
清乾隆年间
(1736 – 1795 年)
广州制造
59 × 30 × 23厘米

广　州　制　造　*Clocks Made in Guangzhou*

This is a decorative object for the living room of a concubine of the emperor. The top part is an oblong mirror with a gilded edge inlaid with red and white precious stones. On top of the mirror is a lotus flower made of a red gemstone. Between the mirror's legs is a revolving bird. Next to the legs are two fountains. The stand is actually a musical box inlaid with a two-hand clock. The scenic paintings on both sides of the dial are decorated with movable figures.

这是清宫后妃居室里的陈设品。主体为一椭圆形容镜，铜镀金边框上镶嵌红白相间的料石，镜顶有一嵌大红石料的宝莲花，在镜的曲腿支架下，有一只能转动的小鸟，制作得形神毕现。支架两旁有两组水法喷泉。底座为乐箱，正中嵌二针时钟。钟的两侧嵌风景图画并装置活动人物。

34

Gilded Copper Clock with Immortal Apes Presenting Birthday Peaches

Qianlong period (1736-1795)
Made in Guangzhou
100 x 40 x 31cm

铜镀金仙猿献桃乐钟
清乾隆年间
(1736 – 1795年)
广州制造
100 × 40 × 31 厘米

Clocks Made in Guangzhou 广 州 制 造

This clock combines the artistic characteristics of both the Chinese and European traditions. According to the imperial archives, it was a gift from the officer in charge of salt import and export at the Guangdong Customs House to Emperor Qianlong on his 70th birthday in 1781.

The top part of the clock consists of a gilded unicorn carrying sacred texts on its back and a three-hand clock crowned with a canopy. The middle part has three apes holding peaches. The lower part is a musical box the front of which is decorated with colorful flower patterns. The two sides have openwork carvings of flowers, trees, grass and shepherds. When activated, music starts, the curtain of the middle part rises, the apes kneel to present the birthday peaches, the colorful flowers revolve and the fountains at the sides spray water, creating a typical joyful atmosphere of a birthday celebration.

此钟造型兼具欧洲和中国传统的艺术特色。据记载，为乾隆七十寿辰(1781年)时粤海关盐督献的寿礼。

钟上层是一象征祥瑞的铜镀金麒麟，背负经卷及三针座钟，上为华盖。中层是三只刻的捧桃猿猴。下层为乐箱，五彩斑斓的转花嵌在箱正面，两旁为雕镂的树木花卉和牧羊人图案。启动后乐声起，中层帘卷，仙猿下跪献寿桃，彩花转动，两边水法如二龙吐水，呈现一派祥瑞热烈的庆寿气氛。

35
Gilded Copper and Enamel-inlaid Clock Supported by a Deer

Qianlong period
(1736-1795)
Made in Guangzhou
103 x 41 x 33cm

铜镀金嵌珐琅鹿驮钟
清乾隆年间
(1736 — 1795 年)
广州制造
103 × 41 × 33 厘米

Clocks Made in Guangzhou 广 州 制 造

Inlaid with colorful enamel, this gilded clock is particularly splendid. When activated, the lower part presents scenes of a dragon spouting water, a phoenix dancing, a man doing acrobatics and the stone flowers at the four corners and on every level revolving all at the same time. The arched gate on the second level automatically opens to reveal a pagoda.

　铜镀金双鹿驮负钟盘。钟座为铜镀金镶嵌彩色珐琅，金碧相映。机械启动后，底层正面的龙喷水、凤飞舞、人翻杠、每层四角、顶部的料石花同时转动；二层正中的拱门自动开启，内呈现一塔。

36
Gilded Copper and Enamel-inlaid Fountain Clock
Qianlong period (1736-1795)
Made in Guangzhou
103 x 35 x 35cm

铜镀金嵌珐琅龙吐水法钟
清乾隆年间
(1736 – 1795年)
广州制造
103 × 35 × 35厘米

广 州 制 造 *Clocks Made in Guangzhou*

The clock assumes the architectural style of traditional Chinese pagodas, with an elegant and gorgeous golden roof, double eaves and gilded carved decorations. From the stand, a huge dragon head, spouting water, supports the pagoda. Inside the tower are the carved images of a man celebrating his birthday and the Eight Immortals. The mechanics of the clock are at the back of the stand. When activated, music plays, the curtain slowly rises and the immortals come out of the pagoda, presenting a scene of great celebration. When the music stops, the immortals retreat into the pagoda.

此钟上部是中国传统楼阁式造型，金顶、重檐、镀金雕花、富丽典雅。底座上一巨大龙头，口衔水法，把楼阁高高托起，似悬于空中。楼阁中有寿星和八仙雕像。钟底座后有控制弦孔。启动后，乐声起，垂帘缓缓卷起，群仙走出阁门，呈现祝寿庆典的盛况。乐止，群仙退回门内。

底座内有机械装置，白色钟盘两旁有二弦孔，钟可走时、报时。

37

Gilded Copper and Enamel Umbrella Clock

*Qianlong period
(1736-1795)
Made in Guangzhou
84 x 37 x 23cm*

铜镀金珐琅翻伞座钟
清乾隆年间
(1736 – 1795 年)
广州制造
84 × 37 × 23 厘米

Clocks Made in Guangzhou 广 州 制 造

The frame of the clock is made of gilded copper and blue enamel decorated with flower patterns of golden thread. The dial is of white enamel and has three hands. To the left of the dial is a doorknob. Behind the door is the mechanical system, which strikes the hour and produces music. The top is shaped like an octagonal silver enamel umbrella. The center of the umbrella supports a fountain surrounded by the image of the Eight Immortals, each holding a treasure. When the clock is activated, music starts, the umbrella opens up, the fountain plays and the stone flowers start revolving. When the music stops, the umbrella folds up.

钟外壳为铜镀金蓝地珐琅金丝缠枝花装饰，钟盘为白珐琅，三指针，计分、计时。钟盘左侧有一个门钮，里面有机械装置，带动钟走时、打时、打乐。钟顶部为银胎珐琅八瓣伞，伞中心是水法，水法周围有八仙雕像，手中各持一宝。上弦后，乐声起，伞瓣撑开，水法转动，如瀑布直泻，同时料石花旋转。乐止，伞合。

38
Gilded Copper Automatic Door Clock Decorated with Five Boys Competing for a Lotus
Qianlong period (1736-1795)
Made in Guangzhou
99 x 45 x 35cm

铜镀金自开门五子夺莲钟
清乾隆
(1736 – 1795 年)
广州制造
99 × 45 × 35 厘米

广　州　制　造　*Clocks Made in Guangzhou*

The frame of the clock is of gilded copper. At the top are two deer supporting the clock on their backs. When the door in the middle part opens, it reveals a crouching dragon. The mobile sculpture of "Five Boys Competing for a Lotus" is a metaphor for a family with many children. On each side is a couplet to the effect that people from all over pay their respects to the owner of the clock, in this case most probably referring to the emperor. When music starts, the door in the middle level opens to reveal a dragon blowing a ball. The boys jump to try to catch the lotus. The flowers in the vases at all three levels as well as decorative spiraling flowers revolve at the same time.

钟体外壳为铜镀金。上部双鹿驮钟；中部门开处一卧龙；底部正中为寓意"多子"的"五子夺莲"活动雕塑，两边是联楹，上书"八方向化，九土来王"。音乐声起后，中门自动打开，卧龙吹球；底部童子跳跃夺莲；上中下三层瓶花、旋转花同时转动。

39
Gilded Copper and Enamel Potted Flower Clock

*Qianlong period
(1736-1795)
Made in Guangzhou
23 x 36 x 30cm*

铜镀金珐琅花盆式钟
清乾隆年间
(1736 – 1795 年)
广州制造
23 × 36 × 30厘米

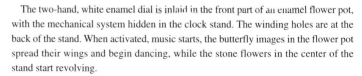

Clocks Made in Guangzhou 广　州　制　造

The two-hand, white enamel dial is inlaid in the front part of an enamel flower pot, with the mechanical system hidden in the clock stand. The winding holes are at the back of the stand. When activated, music starts, the butterfly images in the flower pot spread their wings and begin dancing, while the stone flowers in the center of the stand start revolving.

钟盘嵌在珐琅质花盆正面，为白珐琅二针盘，机械装置在钟底座内。基座后有弦孔，拨动控制弦，乐起，盆中的人造花蝶即开合、飞舞，底座正中的料石花旋转闪亮。

40

**Gilded Copper
Elephant Clock**

*Qianlong period
(1736-95)
Made in Guangzhou
90 x 48 x 19.5cm*

铜镀金转水法太平有象
钟
清乾隆年间
(1736－1795年)
广州制造
90 × 48 × 19.5厘米

广　州　制　造　*Clocks Made in Guangzhou*

The entire body of the clock is made of gilded copper decorated with elegantly carved flowers. What makes it unique is an interesting installation for rolling balls. Eight gilded copper figures with features of Westerners are respectively in charge of sending out the ball, maintaining the rail, carrying the vase and catching the ball. When activated, the ball goes out of the case and follows the preset channel in a repetitive fashion.

The elephant at the top bears a golden vase bearing the characters meaning "great fortune," signifying a period of peace for the Chinese empire.

通体为铜镀金雕花,富丽典雅。其独特之处是在钟的上层安放一套富有趣味的循环滚球装置。八个仿西方人形貌的铜镀金人，分别做送球、擎轨和抱瓶、接球的动作。运转时，球从瓶出，循环往复。

钟的上部为一只象驮着写有"大吉"的金瓶,是利用谐音取意的手法,寓意"太平有象"。

41
Birthday Celebration Screen Clock

Qianlong period
(1736-1795)
Made in Guangzhou
134 x 111 x 26.5cm

群仙祝寿插屏钟
清乾隆年间
(1736 – 1795 年)
广州制造
134 × 111 × 26.5厘米

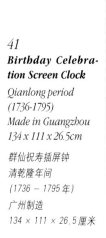

Clocks Made in Guangzhou 广 州 制 造

The clock consists of two levels. The top level is a screen inlaid with precious stones and decorated with bas-relief carvings of hills, pagodas, pavilions, and pine and fruit trees. The Eight Immortals are walking across a stone bridge and monkeys are cavorting in the hills. The lower level is decorated with carved flowers on a gilded copper body. The cavities on both sides of the dial contain movable figures. When activated, the figures move in time to music as if they were going to attend a birthday party.The water is then let out into a brass tank below, and used to refill the top container.

钟分二层，上层插屏是用各种华贵玉石镶嵌的仙山楼阁浮雕，雕有山石、亭台、苍松、果木，八仙行走于石桥上，小猴戏耍于山间。下层为铜镀金雕花钟箱，钟盘两侧孔洞内设有布景及活动人物。上弦启动后，随着乐声，图中人物活动起来，似前往参加祝寿庆典。

42

Sandalwood Clock Decorated with Mother-of-pearl Inlay and Longevity Wishes

Guangxu period (1875-1908)
Made in Guangzhou
86 x 43 x 19cm

紫檀嵌螺钿群仙祝寿钟
清光绪年间
(1875 – 1908 年)
广州制造
86 × 43 × 19 厘米

广 州 制 造 *Clocks Made in Guangzhou*

This was a gift from officials to Empress Dowager Cixi on her 60th birthday.

On the sandalwood frame are patterns of flowers and grass with mother-of-pearl inlay. A white enamel dial is inlaid on a panel with light and elegant openwork enamel patterns. The four corners of the clock are decorated with gilded flower vases. The winding holes are at the back of the clock. A group sculpture of longevity images and doors bearing longevity wishes create an atmosphere of wishing the empress a long life.

为慈禧太后 60 岁生日时，官员所献。

紫檀木钟壳上镶嵌着螺钿组成的花草纹饰，白珐琅钟盘嵌于珐琅镂花面板上，花纹淡雅。钟顶四角均有铜镀金花瓶。弦孔在钟的背面。钟盘上方有一组雕塑，塑有红衣福星、绿衣禄星、持杖老寿星，并有"圣寿无疆"、"尧天"、"舜日"三寿门，呈现出祝寿景象。

43

Gilded Copper Movable Pagoda Clock

*Qianlong period
(1736-1795)
Made in Guangzhou
111 x 47 x 47cm*

铜镀金珐琅升降塔式钟
清乾隆年间
(1736 – 1795 年)
广州制造
111 × 47 × 47厘米

Clocks Made in Guangzhou 广 州 制 造

A seven-story octagonal Buddhist pagoda rests on a pedestal. On the first level is a copper Buddha sculpture. On the second level is an image of the God of Longevity, while the rest of the stories contain Buddhist paintings. On each of the four corners of the stand is a boy carved in ivory standing on a lotus leaf with both palms closed in worship of the Buddha. The pagoda is crowned with a gourd. When the mechanism is activated, the pagoda gradually rises, and the boys bend in prayer.

The front of the clock stand is rendered with blue enamel coiling flowers. In the middle is a two-hand white enamel dial with two winding holes. The rise and fall of the gilded pagoda is controlled by the winding holes at the back of the clock stand.

基座上是八角七层佛塔。一层内置铜佛像，二层是寿星，其余各层为佛像画。塔座四角各有一牙雕童子站在荷叶之上合掌拜佛。塔顶端托一葫芦。机械启动，塔渐渐升起，童子弯腰拜佛。

钟底座正面为蓝珐琅缠枝花纹饰，白珐琅二针钟盘嵌在中间，盘上二弦孔，控制走时、报时。铜镀金塔的升与降，由基座后的弦孔控制。

广　州　制　造　Clocks Made in Guangzhou

44
Gilded Copper and Enamel Gourd-shaped Clock

*Qianlong period
(1736-1795)
Made in Guangzhou
112 x 41 x 33cm*

铜镀金珐琅葫芦式钟
清乾隆年间
(1736 – 1795 年)
广州制造
112 × 41 × 33 厘米

Clocks Made in Guangzhou 广 州 制 造

The dial is inlaid in the lower part of the gourd shape. The upper part of the gourd is an openwork vase with stone flowers. The body of the vase is inlaid with enamel patterns. The middle-lower part of the clock is in the shape of a small stage. At the middle level is a group of sculptures of urban scenes. The lower level also has a set of sculptures, with a man holding a booklet with the Chinese characters meaning "a life as long and fortunate as heaven". At the sides are human figures offering precious gifts, as well as apes, deer, bats and magic herbs -- all symbols of longevity, good fortune and official position. The lower-middle level has revolving fountains on both sides. The mobile decorations all move and stop together with the music.

钟盘嵌于葫芦瓶的腹部，瓶上饰料石花，瓶面镶珐琅花纹。中下层正面皆如一小型舞台，中层布景前为一组都市景象雕塑，底层也为一组雕塑:中间一人手持写有"福寿齐天"的摺子，旁边有众多献宝人及猿、鹿、蝙蝠、灵芝等，寓"福禄寿"之意。中下层两侧均有转动的水法。图景及插花均随乐声启止而动静。

78

45
Gilded Copper Stone-inlaid Mirror Clock

Qianlong period
(1736-1795)
Made in Guangzhou
100 x 64cm

铜镀金嵌料石花镜嵌表
清乾隆 (1736 – 1795 年)
广州制造
100 × 64 厘米

广 州 制 造 *Clocks Made in Guangzhou*

An oblong mirror is inlaid in a frame of gilded copper with grass patterns. The mirror was put on the dressing tables of palace concubines. At the top of the mirror is a white enamel dial which was made in Britain. Its mechanical part contains springs, a cone pulley and chains which activate the clock.

椭圆形容镜嵌在饰铜镀金卷草花纹的边框内，镜可放在梳妆台上，供宫中后妃梳妆时用。容镜上方嵌有白珐琅表盘，上有计分、计时数字。表内机芯由发条盒、塔轮、链条组成，带动表走动，表为英国制造。

46

Gilded Copper and Inlaid Enamel Longevity Clock

Qianlong period (1736-1795)
Made in Guangzhou
108 x 44 x 38cm

铜镀金嵌珐琅楼式万寿无疆钟

清乾隆年间

(1736 – 1795 年)

广州制造

108 × 44 × 38 厘米

Clocks Made in Guangzhou 广 州 制 造

This clock is modeled after a three-story European building. The lower and middle levels are rendered with blue enamel patterns of coiling flowers. The edges have gilded flower patterns. At the middle level is a gilded Buddhist pagoda which can rise and fall. On each side of the pagoda is an immortal with wings, praying with both palms pressed together. On the lower level is the dial between fountains and boys holding flowers. When activated, the person in the pavilion at the top level comes to the front of the gate to display a booklet on which is written a wish for longevity. Meanwhile, the Buddhist pagoda in the middle gradually rises and the winged immortal prostrates himself in prayer. The flower-holding boy, fountains at the lower level and the flowers at both the middle and upper levels revolve all at the same time. When the music stops, they all stop moving.

钟的造型为一欧式风格的三层楼亭。一、二层壳面为蓝珐琅缠枝花饰，周边为铜镀金花饰。中层内是可升降的九层镀金佛塔，塔两边各站一带翅仙人合掌作拜佛状；底层钟盘两旁是捧花的童子，并伴有水法。启动时，上层亭内一人手捧写有"万寿无疆"摺子走至门前，将其展开，同时，中门佛塔缓缓升起，两侧带翅仙人躬身拜佛，下层花童、水法及中、上层插花均同时转动。乐止，一切恢复原状。

47
Gilded Copper and Inlaid Enamel Longevity Wishes Clock
Qianlong period (1736-1795)
Made in Guangzhou
97 x 44 x 38cm

铜镀金嵌珐琅飞人献福寿钟
乾隆年间
(1736 – 1795 年)
广州制造
97 × 44 × 38 厘米

广 州 制 造 *Clocks Made in Guangzhou*

The gilded copper and enamel-inlaid clock body has three levels. At the top level, a dial is inlaid in the belly of a flower vase. The dial is decorated with white enamel and has three hands. The winding holes are at the back. The lower level is where the mechanical system is located. When the clock is activated, the hammer-holding figure in the pavilion at the middle level strikes a bell. The curtain of the middle door at the lower level now rolls up, and a winged figure comes forward, kneels and reveals two characters meaning longevity and good fortune originally sealed in a peach. The figures on both sides tumble over horizontal bars. The flower in the vase at the top level turns and butterflies flutter until the music stops.

This clock, representative of those produced in Guangzhou, was a birthday gift to the emperor.

铜镀金蓝地珐琅钟体，分为三层。钟盘嵌于上层花瓶的瓶腹上，为白珐琅盘，三针，钟后板上有弦孔。底层有机械装置，将三层机械玩意连成一体，启动后，中层亭内持锤人有节奏地敲打钟碗，演奏乐曲；在乐声中，底层中门门帘卷起，带翅人向前移动，双腿跪下，双手捧的桃子分开，露出"福寿"两字，左右门内攀杠人作翻杠动作，同时上层瓶中花束转动，蝴蝶飞舞，乐终，一切停止。

此钟为给皇帝祝寿的礼品，是广州钟表中的佳品。

48
Gilded Copper Bird Pavilion Clock

Guangxu period
(1875-1908)
Made in Suzhou
131 x 69 x 44cm

铜镀金鸟音亭式钟
清光绪年间
(1875 – 1908 年)
苏州制造
131 × 69 × 44 厘米

Clocks Made in Suzhou 苏 州 制 造

Above the three-hand dial plate is an automatic door, behind which is a revolving flower. Below the dial are three discs. The one on the left shows the week from Monday to Sunday, while the one on the right is marked with the 12 months. The one in the middle is marked with the 12 traditional divisions of the day, and has an installation simulating the rising and setting of the sun and moon. It also displays the phases of the moon.

There is a bird in the pavilion at the top of the clock. When the clock is fully wound, the bird opens its mouth to sing beautifully, and shakes its head and tail.

为三针时钟，正面钟盘上方，是自动开闭的方门，内装转花。钟盘下有三个圆盘：左边是星期一至星期日的"周盘"；右边是一至十二月的"年历"；中间圆盘有十二时辰和北极恒星图，内有模拟日月升落的装置，并能显示月亮的圆缺变化。这些天象的变化随时钟走动而显现。

钟顶亭内站一只鸟，上弦后，发出清脆悦耳的叫声，并张口，摇头，摆尾。

苏 州 制 造 *Clocks Made in Suzhou*

49
Gilded Copper Magic Clock with Automatic Door

*Guangxu period
(1875-1908)
Made in Suzhou
75 x 40 x 30cm*

铜镀金自开门变戏法钟
清光绪年间
(1875 – 1908 年)
苏州制造
75 × 40 × 30 厘米

Underneath the clock is an automatic door. When the clock is set in motion, the door opens to reveal a figure who puts a bell upside down on a table and picks up a bouquet of flowers. It repeats the motion with the bell to produce different kinds of flower bouquets four times, and then the door closes automatically. The stand of the clock is a musical box, in front of which is a fountain with walking figures. The four corners of the stand have gilded flowers that revolve.

　　铜镀金外壳，钟下有一自动开关门，启动机械装置门开，门内出现一人，将铃扣于桌上，当提起时变出一束鲜花；然后再扣变出其它花束。如此四次，门即自动关闭。钟的底座是乐箱，正面框内是水法装置，前有行走的小人。底座上四角有铜镀金转花。

50
Sandalwood Clock with Polaris Constellation and Lunar Terms

*Guangxu period
(1875-1908)
Made in Suzhou
66 x 37.2 x 37.2cm*

紫檀木北极恒星图时辰
节气钟
清光绪年间
(1875 – 1908 年)
苏州制造
66 × 37.2 × 37.2厘米

Clocks Made in Suzhou 苏 州 制 造

The sandalwood frame of the clock rests on an openwork stand. A black dial is inlaid in the frame. Its long hand points to the 12 traditional divisions of the day on the outer ring, while the short one points at the 24 lunar terms marked on the inner ring. There are two sets of mechanical systems that operate the clock.

On the black dial, the constellations are described in gold.

紫檀木外壳，镂花支架，圆形钟壳内嵌着黑色钟盘，钟盘有二指针，长针指向外沿的十二时辰，短针指内圈的二十四节气，钟内有二组机械系统带动钟的运行。

黑地钟盘上，用金字刻写三垣、二十八星宿和诸多星座，构成一幅北极恒星图，作为装饰。

51
Gilded Copper Clock Decorated with Lions Supporting a Flower Pot

Made in 1768, London
By James Cox
73 x 24 x 24cm

铜镀金狮驮嵌螺钿方花
盆表
公元1768年制造
英国伦敦
詹姆斯·考克斯
(James Cox)制
73 × 24 × 24厘米

英　国　钟　表　British Clocks and Watches

This gilded copper clock is mounted on a two-tier white stone stand the edges of which are decorated with artificial stones and mother-of-pearl. This in turn is mounted on a wooden stand covered with red velvet. Four lions carry on their backs a flower pot on which are four exotic animals. In the middle sits a child holding a bouquet of flowers. A clock is inlaid in the flower bouquet. Springs support a butterfly and a dragonfly. When the mechanical system in the flower pot is activated, a boat with a boatman moves around the pot, and the butterfly and dragonfly flutter. The winding key bears the inscription "James Cox 1768".

铜镀金质。在铺衬着红色丝绒的木托座上，有假宝石螺钿镶边的白石底座二层。座上四只雄狮背负着白石花盆，盆沿上攀伏四只怪兽，中间坐着一个手举花束的儿童，花朵间嵌一只小表，弹簧支撑着花束间的蝴蝶和蜻蜓。盆里装置着机械零件，启动后，花盆四面布景里船行、小人走动，连接在弹簧上的蝴蝶和蜻蜓微微颤动摇晃。上弦的钥匙上刻有"James Cox"和"1768"字样。

52
Gilded Copper Chiming Clock with Four Lions Supporting a Fountain

Made in 1771, London
By James Cox
82 x 38 x 32cm

铜镀金四狮驮水法乐钟
公元 1771 年制造
英国伦敦
詹姆斯·考克斯
(James Cox)制
82 × 38 × 32 厘米

British Clocks and Watches 英 国 钟 表

Four lions support a square stand upon which the gilded clock is mounted. The stand bears the inscription "J. Cox, 1771, London". When the clock is wound up by pulling a string, music starts and a boat in the stand moves in water produced by a fountain on the middle level.

铜镀金质。四只站立着的雄狮驮着塔的方形底座。塔尖上用红白人造钻石缀成的多角星的中心嵌着一只小钟，钟下托座的四周书写有"J COX"、"1771"、"London"、"Feclt"字样，拉绳上弦后，乐声响起，底层布景中的船在水中行驶，中层水法似瀑布奔流。

53
Gilded Copper Rectangular Clock Decorated with a Cow

Made about 1780, London
By James Cox
43 x 54 x 33cm

铜镀金立牛长方座钟
约1780年制造
英国伦敦
詹姆斯·考克斯
(James Cox)制造
43 × 54 × 33厘米

英　国　钟　表　*British Clocks and Watches*

This gilded clock is rectangular and has three dials, registering the minutes, quarters and hours. The mechanical system consists of a spring, a cone pulley and chains. At the back is a musical device. In the two indented sides are oil paintings portraying seaside town scenery. When the clock is activated, miniature figures and boats in front of the oil paintings move. A golden cow stands under a lush palm tree on top of the clock.

　　钟的主体部分为一装饰华美的铜镀金长方形钟箱,钟箱正前面有计时、计刻、计分三个表盘。时盘上有属名,机芯以发条盒、塔轮、链条三部分组成动力源,带动齿轮传送系统。箱后面有乐曲转换器。两侧凹进的方框内嵌有描绘海滨城镇风光的油画。上弦启动后,画前的微型人物、船只行走。钟箱上部塑有一头金色的母牛站立在翠绿的棕榈树下,目视前方。

54
Gilded Copper Square Bird Cage Clock

Made in 1783, London
By James Cox
76 x 32 x 32cm

铜镀金四方形鸟笼表
1783 年制造
英国伦敦
詹姆斯·考克斯
(James Cox)制
76 × 32 × 32 厘米

British Clocks and Watches 英 国 钟 表

This clock is in the shape of an elegant bird cage. A star with two intertwined flowers of red and green at the top of the cage sends out radiating lights. The star is made of inlaid red glass on a gilded copper background. The stand of the bird cage has eight corners. Underneath is a red lacquer box containing the mechanism. The front part of the cage stand is inlaid with a small dial decorated with gilded flowers on both sides. The cage has 12 pillars in the form of trees. Between the pillars are 48 gilded wires. The middle of the cage is decorated with gilded leaves. The center of the lower part of the cage is a spiraling pagoda inlaid with green and pink glass. A painted copper bird sits on a horizontal bar in the cage.

When the clock is fully wound, the bird spreads its wings, turns left and right, jumps between two bars and sings, accompanied by music. The star turns alternately to both sides, and sends forth rays. A tube at the back of the cage opens, and a glass fountain creates a waterfall.

钟体制成鸟笼形状,十分精致,鸟笼顶端为红绿两层交错旋转的团花组成的宝星花,其周围放射的光芒,是用铜镀金全底托嵌红玻璃制成。鸟笼底座呈八角形,座箱四周繫紫红漆,内放置机械结构,正面嵌一小表,饰以铜镀金花环。笼子以十二棵菠萝树为柱,柱之间用四十八根铜镀金丝,编制而成。中腰有镀金缠枝叶围绕,鸟笼底部中心是嵌粉红和绿玻璃的螺旋塔,笼后有一可以开合的圆筒。一只铜质彩绘小鸟立于笼中横杆上。

上弦后,在乐曲声中,小鸟展翅摆动并左右转身,在两横杆上往返跳动,发出鸣叫声;顶部的宝星花红绿交错,左右旋转,似光芒四射的星光;笼后圆筒门开启,转动玻璃水法,形成瀑布流泻。乐止,一切停止。

55
Gilded Copper Clock with Rhinoceroses

*Supporting Cosmetics
Box and Mirror
Made 1764-71, London
By James Cox
73 x 36 x 24cm*

铜镀金犀牛驮容镜规矩
箱表

*1764 年－ 1771 年制造
英国伦敦
詹姆斯·考克斯
(James Cox)制
73 × 36 × 24 厘米*

British Clocks and Watches 英 国 钟 表

Four rhinoceroses carry a gilded copper box decorated with red agates with an elegant design and superb workmanship. Under the slanting cover is a box for cosmetics. On top of the box are two gilded soldiers standing on the left and right sides, respectively, supporting a mirror with a flower- and grass-patterned edge in gilded copper. The mirror's angle can be adjusted. On top of the mirror is a dial with two hands. A miniature figure in painted enamel is located in the center of the dial. When the clock is activated, the figure moves and a flower over the dial revolves.

　　四只犀牛背驮着铜镀金嵌红玛瑙箱，纹饰精细、工巧。打开坡形箱盖，里边可以摆放各种化妆用品。箱上部左右各有一铜镀金人，手持武器，支撑着一面镜子，镜子周围饰铜镀金花草纹，镜子的角度可以自由调节，镜上置一表，有长短针，表盘中间有珐琅彩绘人物。启动后，人物活动，转花旋转。

56
Gilded Copper Clock Decorated with Agate and Revolving Flowers

Made in 1766, London
By James Cox
50 x 23 x 18cm

铜镀金嵌玛瑙转花表
1766 年
英国伦敦
詹姆斯·考克斯
(James Cox) 制造
50 × 23 × 18 厘米

Four gilded lions support a musical box of gilded copper inlaid with agate. Images of ancient Greek deities are carved on the box. On each of the four corners of the box is a gilded copper vase containing flowers embellished with jade beads. In the center is a double-eared vase with an elephant-foot stand. In this vase is a bouquet of flowers made of green and red gemstones and crystal beads. A large flower in the middle bears a small dial. When the clock is activated, the musical box plays a tune and the flowers in the vase revolve.

此表镀金镶翠，装饰绚丽繁复。四只铜镀金雄狮背负着铜镀金嵌玛瑙乐箱，乐箱雕有古希腊神话中的爱神和森林神，四角铜镀金瓶中插着珠翠镶嵌的花束。中心为一象足双耳瓶，瓶中插一束红绿料石和晶莹的珠子制成的装饰花，其中一朵硕大的花中嵌一只小表。表单独上弦，上弦启动后，箱中发出悦耳乐声，同时瓶中花朵交错转动。

57
Gilded Copper Clock on Square Agate Stand with Two Boys

Made in 1765, London
By James Cox
31.6 x 8 x 6cm; 4.8cm in diameter

铜镀金镶玛瑙双童方座表
1765 年制造
英国伦敦
詹姆斯 · 考克斯
(James Cox) 制
31.6 × 8 × 6 厘米
表直径 4.8 厘米

British Clocks and Watches 英 国 钟 表

The clock's stand is a square musical box of gilded copper inlaid with agate. The front part of the stand has two winding holes, and each of the four corners is decorated with a gorgeously dressed girl. On each side of the musical box stands a charming boy. The clock is motivated by springs, a cone pulley and gears. At the back of the clock is a pendulum. The clock is crowned with a flower made of pearls. The clock has two elegant keys bearing the inscription "James Cox 1765".

The technology of making locks and keys in 18th century Britain was very advanced and enjoyed widespread fame in Europe. This is why when a clock was made, elegant keys and key rings were made to go with it. The keys and key rings then became fashionable personal accessories for the nobility.

钟座为铜镀金镶玛瑙方形乐箱，箱的正面有两个上弦孔，四角塑有四个裙裾飘逸的女子立像，箱台面两侧站立两个憨态可掬的儿童，表的机芯以发条、塔轮、齿轮为动力源，带动齿轮传送系统，表的背面为明摆，顶端有珠花。表有两把精致的钥匙，分别镂刻着"Jas Cox"和"1765年"字样。

18世纪，英国的制锁和制钥匙工艺十分精致，闻名于欧洲，所以在制造钟表的同时，也设计了十分美丽精巧的钥匙和钥匙链，成为当时贵族和帝王崇尚的一种装饰。

58

Wooden Tower Whistling Clock Decorated with Flower Patterns

Made in the 18th century, London
By James Newton
48 x 33 x 22cm

木楼嵌铜花木哨乐钟
18 世纪
英国伦敦詹姆斯·牛顿
（James Neraton）制造
48 × 33 × 22 厘米

On the front part of this wooden tower clock with copper decorations is a two-hand dial, above which is a lacquer landscape painting.

A spring and cone pulley activate the clock using a thread made of gut, i.e., the speed of the escape wheel is controlled by the winding wheel. When fully wound, the mechanical parts pump air into an air bag connected to ten whistles. The mouths of the whistles are opened and closed by a wooden roller. Different tunes can be played, and a windmill, ox, sheep and human figures painted above the dial turn with the music.

　　木楼嵌铜花钟壳，正面为二针表盘，表盘上方嵌有一幅表现异国田园放牧的漆画。
　　其机械构造有发条盒、塔轮，通过皮弦（即羊肠拧成的线）为动力源，即轴擒纵器由风轮控制快慢。上弦后，由动力源搅扛，搅扛带动气袋闭合，充气入聚气袋，连接十根有舌簧的木哨，木哨上方有带铜刺的木滚筒，滚筒转动触到木哨上的铜丝，铜丝控制舌簧开闭。舌簧开启，气袋中气流入木哨；簧闭，发出声响。由于木哨长短、粗细、舌簧各异，发出的声响也不同，随着滚筒的转动，奏出和谐的乐曲，表盘上方所绘的风车，牛羊及人物也随着乐曲声转动。

59
Mahogany Calendar Double Dial Clock

Made in the 18th century, London
By James Smith
43 x 29 x 21.5cm

红木楼式带日历两套钟
18 世纪
英国伦敦
詹姆斯·史密斯
(James Smith) 制造
高 43 × 29 × 21.5厘米

British Clocks and Watches 英 国 钟 表

Set in a mahogany frame is a white enamel dial with flower patterns of gilded copper. The two-hand dial bears a calendar indicating the dates. There are two winding holes on the dial. On one side is a string which, when pulled, indicates the time. The dial also carries the name "James Smith". Smith studied clock making in London around 1743, and was a member of the Clockmakers Association of London from 1751 to 1762.

红木钟壳, 铜镀金錾花钟面, 白珐琅钟盘。钟为两针, 带日历。表盘上有两个上弦孔, 机芯有发条盒、塔轮、链条。上弦后, 可走时。在钟的一侧有一绳子, 只要拽一下绳子, 便能报出时间, 具有问钟的性能。钟盘上刻有 "James Smith" 的名字。詹姆斯·史密斯于 1743 年在伦敦学习制钟技术, 1751 年 — 1762 年成为英国伦敦钟表协会的成员。

60

***Gilded Copper
Rockery Clock with
Swimming Swans***

*Made about 1775,
London*
By Timothy Williamson
73 x 65 x 42cm

铜镀金假山跑鸭水法钟
约1775年
英国伦敦　威廉森
(Williamson)制造
73 × 65 × 42 厘米

英　国　钟　表　*British Clocks and Watches*

The stand is in the shape of a hill, with caves in the lower part. On top of the hill are palm trees and an octagonal pavilion. A white enamel clock dial with hands for the seconds, minutes and hours, as well as a calendar, is inlaid in the center of the hill. On the hill are figures of a crane, bird, sheep, ox, lion, rabbit, dog, snake, alligator, lizard, shells and snails. The mirror surface in the cave symbolizes a pool on which two swans are swimming. They are held in place by a magnet. In the pavilion are two figures holding hammers to strike a suspended bell. The clock is wound by pulling a string. Then music starts, the flowers by the pavilion and the two pillars revolve, and the swans start swimming in the pool.

　　钟座制成山石状，下方有洞穴，顶部有棕榈树数株和八角亭一座。山石正中嵌一钟。钟盘是白珐琅质，上有时、分、秒针和日历针。山石上下雕有仙鹤、鸟、羊、牛、狮、兔、狗、蛇、鳄鱼、蜥蜴以及贝类、螺蛳等。山洞中以镜面为水池，两只游嬉的天鹅以磁石牵引游动。八角亭中，左右各坐一人，手持钟锤，按时敲击悬挂着的钟碗。拉动绳弦启动后，乐曲声起，两侧柱顶和亭上的花束旋转，天鹅在水池中绕游嬉戏。

61

***Gilded Copper
Flower Pot Clock***

*Made around 1780,
London*

By Timothy Williamson

67.7 x 32 x 32cm

铜镀金花盆式嵌料石花
表

约1780年

英国伦敦

提摩泰·威廉森

(Timothy Williamson)

制造

67.7 × 32 × 32厘米

British Clocks and Watches   英   国   钟   表

Timothy Williamson was from a family with a history of clock making. His grandfather, Joseph Williamson, was a leading clock maker during the reign of Queen Anne (1702-14).

The stand of this clock takes the shape of a flower pot, the bottom and edge of which are decorated with elegant flower patterns. The sides of the pot are inlaid with glass, within which is a landscape painting. In front of the painting are movable figures. The top part of the flower pot is shaped in the forms of hills, and decorated with flowers and leaves made of green, red and white gemstones. Standing on a rockery is a two-hand chime clock. The winding holes are on the side of the flower pot. When the clock is fully wound, the figures start to move, and the stone flowers quiver gently.

　　威廉森氏是英国有名的钟表世家。提摩泰的祖父约瑟夫·威廉森(Joseph Williamson)是英国安妮女王时期(1702－1714年)有名的钟表匠师，一生工作十分勤奋，1725年死在他的工作间里。提摩泰·威廉森是18世纪末的钟表名匠。

　　铜镀金的钟座造型为一花盆，底部和周沿雕刻着华美的纹饰。盆壁周围嵌玻璃，玻璃框内为城镇风光画，画前有能活动的人物，花盆的上部雕成山石状，并装饰着红、绿、白料石嵌成的花、叶。假山石中嵌一两针报时表。在花盆边有上弦孔，上弦后，玻璃框中景前的人物在齿轮的带动下转动，连接在弹簧上的料石花随之微微颤动。

62
Triangular Wooden Tower Musical Clock Supported by Lions

Made 1780-1795, London
By Timothy Williamson
100 x 54 x 54cm

狮驮木楼三角形音乐钟
约 1780 – 1795 年
英 国 伦 敦　 威 廉 森
(Williamson) 制造
100 × 54 × 54 厘米

On each of the three sides of this clock is a while enamel, two-hand dial activated by a mechanical system. On the indented part above the dial is a painted country scene, in front of which are movable figures. The clock is crowned with a fountain containing dolphins. When the clock is activated, the fountain turns, and so do the flowers at the three corners. The figures in the indented part also move.

　　钟体的三面皆有白珐琅质两针表盘，里边有一套机芯，带动三面针走时。盘上孔洞内有乡村风景画，景前有活动的人物，顶端装置有海豚喷水造型的水法。钟启动后，水法旋转似喷泉，三面各角花饰转动，孔洞内的人物走动。

英 国 钟 表 *British Clocks and Watches*

63

Gilded Copper Chiming Clock with Moving Figures and Pillars

Made 1780-1795, London
By Timothy Williamson
79.5 x 40 x 36.5cm

铜镀金自开门转人转柱乐钟
约 1780 – 1795 年
英国伦敦　威廉森
(Williamson) 制造
79.5 × 40 × 36.5厘米

The clock is in the shape of a three-story tower with four gilded pillars, around which dragons coil at each story. The roof ridges are decorated with dinosaurs. The front part of the tower is inlaid with enamel paintings of European ladies. At the top story is a two-hand dial. The doors with images of ladies at the second story can automatically open to reveal a cosmetics box. When the clock is activated, music starts, and the doors open to reveal walking figures inside. At the same time, the pillars revolve.

　　钟体为铜镀金三层楼阁式。每层均有四根镀金蟠龙柱，脊角上爬伏着口衔铜铃的翼龙，楼的面上镶嵌着欧洲古典仕女肖像珐琅画。上层正面为二针时钟；第二层嵌仕女肖像画的门能自动打开；下层为一妆奁匣。启动后，在乐曲声中，第二层门自动打开，内有人物走动，龙柱转动。

64
Gilded Copper Clock with Writing Figure

Made about 1770, London
By Timothy Williamson
231 x 77 x 77cm

铜镀金写字人钟
约1770 年
英国伦敦 威廉森
(Williamson) 制造
231 × 77 × 77 厘米

British Clocks and Watches 英 国 钟 表

Four carved wooden legs support a coffee table on which is a gilded four-story copper tower. In a pavilion on the top story two figures are holding a tubular object. When the clock is activated, the two figures move apart, to produce a horizontal banner with the characters for "long life". In the second story from the top is a musician who is capable of lowering and turning his head. At 3:00, 6:00, 9:00 and 12:00, he strikes a bell, and music plays. At the third story is a while enamel dial with two hands. In the pavilion at the lowest level is a copper figure whose head is carved out of ivory. His clothes suggest that he is a European gentleman. Half-kneeling, he is in the act of writing. When the mechanical system is activated, he writes eight Chinese characters to the effect that all people respect the owner of the clock. With the rise and fall of the writing brush, the man lowers his head, and turns it to the left and right.

The mechanism controlling the figure is hidden under the stand of the tower, consisting of three plates with indented edges. The movements of the three plates activate the figure to write up and down and from left to right. This large and elegant clock with a very complicated mechanism was made especially for the imperial palace.

　　木雕花曲腿方几上有铜镀金四层楼阁。最上层圆亭中两人举一筒状物,启动后二人分升,展示"万寿无疆"四字的横幅。第二层是一奏乐人,能低头转颈,每逢3、6、9、12时敲钟打乐。第三层有一白珐琅钟盘的二针时乐钟。最下层亭内有一铜人,头部用象牙雕成,形貌服饰似欧洲绅士。铜人单腿跪地,一手扶案,一手握毛笔,当机械启动后,提笔书写"八方向化,九土来王"八个汉字,并随着笔锋的起落,做出低头、左右转动的姿态。

　　操纵铜人写字的机械都在亭座和雕花几下面,内部构造为三个圆盘,盘的边缘有凸凹处,长短距离不一样,都是按照八个汉字的笔画笔锋特制。三盘分别操纵上下动作即提笔落笔、横写和竖写。这是一件机械结构比较复杂,专门为宫廷制作的大型精美的钟。

65
Gilded Copper Grapevine Clock

Made 1780-1795, London

By Timothy Williamson

54 x 24 x 24cm

铜镀金葡萄架铜人举表

1780 – 1795 年

英国伦敦

威廉森(Williamson)制造

54 × 24 × 24 厘米

British Clocks and Watches 英 国 钟 表

The gilded copper stand contains a musical box and the mechanical parts of the clock. The glass frame of the stand is embellished with three figures in a landscape. The stand is also carved with three silver goats, a Chinese symbol for good fortune. On the stand is a grapevine with grapes made of pearls. Sitting on the grapevine are birds and butterflies. A gilded copper girl sits on a rock holding in her right hand a two-hand, silver-cased enamel dial. On the back of the dial is the name "Williamson". Behind the figure is a revolving fountain. The clock is wound up at the back of the stand. When the clock is activated, music starts, the figures in the painting start moving, the fountain revolves, and the butterflies and birds flap their wings.

　　铜镀金底座里有音乐装置和带动各部件的机械，底座前的玻璃框中嵌有三幅人物风景画。底座上雕有三只银色山羊，称为"三阳开泰"寓意吉祥。底座上有一座葡萄架，挂有用小珍珠穿成葡萄串，架上还有葡萄枝叶和停落的小鸟和蝴蝶，石台上有一位神态端庄的铜镀金女坐像，右手举着一只银壳珐琅两针小表，表的机芯背板上署有"Williamson"字样，人像身后有转动的水法。在底座的后面上弦，启动后，乐曲声响起，风景人物画中的人物行走，水法转动，蝴蝶和小鸟也展翅颤动。

66

Gilded Copper Clock Decorated with Revolving Flowers, Phoenix and Fountain

Made 1780-1795, London
By Timothy Williamson
108 x 66 x 53cm

铜镀金嵌珐琅转花鸟音
水法钟
约 1780 – 1795 年
英国伦敦
威廉森（Williamson）制造
108 × 66 × 53 厘米

British Clocks and Watches　英 国 钟 表

The stand of the clock is a musical box which also contains all the mechanical parts. The four sides of the stand are embellished with 10 enamel paintings featuring birds and European ladies. On top of the stand is a miniature garden decorated with trees, flowers, sheep, sparrows, swans, towers and a fountain. In the center is a three-hand dial, on top of which sits a phoenix. In classical Chinese fairy tales, the phoenix is the queen of all the birds. Here, the other birds are admiring the phoenix, symbolizing good luck and a happy life. This theme indicates that the clock was made especially for the imperial court of the Qing Dynasty.

　　钟的底座为乐箱,控制各部分的机械也安置在里面。底座的四面嵌有以欧洲古典仕女和禽鸟为题材的珐琅画,共 10 幅。底座的台面上俨然是一处微缩的园景、料珠、金属等制成的花树、小羊、莺雀、天鹅、塔柱、喷泉等配置有序。居中为一三针时钟,钟上栖息着一只凤鸟。凤鸟是中国古代传说中的鸟王,它与众多的禽鸟构成一幅"百鸟朝凤"的景致,寓意吉祥美好,由此可见此钟是专为清代宫廷制作的。
　　底座内的机械启动后,枝头小鸟鸣叫,泉水喷涌,花朵转动,出现了生机勃勃的热烈场面。

67

Gilded Copper Tower Clock Decorated with Peacock Fanning Its Tail

Made in the 18th century, London
By Timothy Williamson
59 x 33.5 x 16cm

铜镀金牌楼式孔雀开屏钟

18世纪

英国伦敦

威廉森 (Williamson) 制造

59 × 33.5 × 16厘米

British Clocks and Watches　英　国　钟　表

The center of the stand containing the music box is inlaid with paintings in blue, green and white enamel of a hall in Western architectural style. The enamel paintings on each side portray sculptors. Between two enamel pillars on the stand is a three-hand dial supporting a small pavilion. In the pavilion, a standing figure is holding a copper hammer to strike the time. His strikes are followed by music, and the peacock spreads its tail. A shepherdess and her three sheep move at the same time.

　　钟底层乐箱的正面镶嵌着由蓝、绿、白珐琅组成的画，画面为一西式厅堂内景。两侧各嵌有表现艺术家从事雕塑创作的珐琅画。箱上两珐琅柱间架着三针时钟，钟上有一小亭，亭下站着一持锤铜人，到时敲钟碗报时，而后乐曲声起，孔雀开屏，牧羊女和三只羊儿也在机械的带动下做出相应的动作。

68

Gilded Copper Clock Supported by a Sheep

Made 1780-1795, London

By Timothy Williamson

79 x 63 x 53cm

铜镀金羊驮钟

约 1780 – 1795 年

英国伦敦

威廉森（Williamson）制造

79 × 63 × 53 厘米

A sheep is a symbol of a wish for prosperity during the New Year in Chinese folklore. The shepherd here, however, looks like a Westerner. The sheep carries on its back a red box whose front features a two-hand dial. Nestled in a tree with golden branches and jade leaves is a partridge. The mechanical parts are hidden in the belly of the sheep. When the clock strikes, music plays, and the partridge flaps its wings and starts to sing.

钟的创意依然采用中国传统的"三阳开泰"题材，但牧童的形貌却仿西方人塑造。大羊背驮一只制作精美的红色箱子，其正面嵌有一两针钟。箱上金枝翠叶的树丛中栖息着一只报时鹧鸪鸟。机械装置在大羊的腹内，每逢报时，机械启动，音乐声十分动听，鹧鸪鸟翅膀抖动，发出"咕、咕"的叫声，打几时叫几声。

69
Gilded Copper and Enamel Pocket Watch

Made during 1780 and 1795, London
By Williamson
5.1cm in diameter and 2.8cm in thickness

铜镀金嵌珐琅画怀表
约 1780 – 1795 年
英国伦敦
威廉森 (Williamson) 制造
直径 5.1 厘米
厚 2.8 厘米

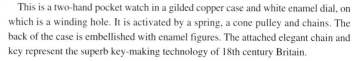

British Clocks and Watches　英　国　钟　表

This is a two-hand pocket watch in a gilded copper case and white enamel dial, on which is a winding hole. It is activated by a spring, a cone pulley and chains. The back of the case is embellished with enamel figures. The attached elegant chain and key represent the superb key-making technology of 18th century Britain.

　　此怀表为铜镀金二针表。表盘为白珐琅，中间有一上弦的孔。表的机芯有发条盒、塔轮、链条组成动力源。珐琅表壳后面有人物珐琅画。此表附有精美的钥匙和表链，它代表了 18 世纪英国钥匙工艺的高超技艺。

70
**Gilded Copper Tower
Clock on Horseback**

*Made during the 18th
century, London*
By William Vale
138 x 58 x 52cm

铜镀金四马驮亭式平放
钟盘钟
18 世纪
英国伦敦 威廉·维尔
(William Vale) 制造
138 × 58 × 52厘米

英 国 钟 表 *British Clocks and Watches*

The entire body of this clock is beautifully gilded. Four galloping copper horses carry a musical box which has a painting of a country landscape. In front of the painting are movable figures. Above the musical box are three stories of a tower. Three dials are mounted at the lowest story. They tell the seconds, minutes and hours. Behind them are seven dragons spouting water. In the pavilion on the second story are two figures for striking the quarters, and four fish spouting water. In the pavilion at the top story is a figure which strikes the hours.

钟通体镀金。下部为四匹铜奔马驮乐箱，箱内正面嵌有乡村风景画，画前有活动人物。箱上有三层亭子，最下层前沿有三个平放的钟盘，可走时、走分、走秒，其后有七条龙头喷水柱；中层亭的左右各站一敲钟碗的人，专管报刻，中间有四条鱼吐水柱；最上层的亭内站一敲钟碗人，专管报时。

71
Gilded Copper Tower Chiming Clock with Dancing Figures

Made in about 1770-1805, London
By William Carpenter
96 x 55 x 37cm

铜镀金牌楼式舞人音乐钟
约1770 – 1805 年
英国伦敦
威廉·卡本特
(William Carpenter)制造
96 × 55 × 37 厘米

British Clocks and Watches 英 国 钟 表

This clock is characterized by dense decorative patterns, a striking contrast of colors and prominence given to its main part. In the round frame in the middle is a two-hand dial flanked by a small dial on each side, one to control the striking of the hours and the other to control the music. Below the dial is a colored enamel painting featuring the Prince Regent's house in London. A copper figure holding hammers in the pavilion at the top part of the clock strikes the quarters with both hands, and the hours with one hand. The frame, supported by curved legs, is decorated with green leaves and two exquisite small copper figures. Four gilded copper elephants hold up the stand. When the clock is activated, music plays, the figures in the enamel painting walk and dance, and the flowers revolve.

　　此钟纹饰繁密，金碧交映，主体突出。中部的圆形钟壳上部有二针表盘，两旁各有一小盘，一个指示停止敲钟，一个指示交换几个乐曲；钟面下方是珐琅彩画，所画为英国王子瑞金特(Regent)在伦敦的卡尔顿别墅。钟壳上方亭内有一双手持锤的敲钟铜人，双手时是打刻，单手敲时为打时。钟壳下方的曲腿支架上饰有绿色枝叶和两个制作精美的小铜人，钟体下有四只铜镀金象作足。启动后，乐起，珐琅画中的人物走动并起舞，珠花转动，到一定时间打刻、打时。

72
Clock with Gilded Copper Elephant and Lion Tamer

Made in 1790, London
By John Vale
100 x 44 x 33cm

铜镀金人戏狮象驮钟
1790 年
英国伦敦　约翰·维尔
(John Vale) 制造
100 × 44 × 33 厘米

British Clocks and Watches　英　国　钟　表

This gilded copper clock consists of three stories. The lowest story is a musical box whose front resembles a small theater stage with props, fountain, figures and potted flowers. At the center of the musical box is an elevated glass terrace with two elephants supporting the clock. In the center of the dial is a hand for indicating the seconds. Above is an hour dial while below are two dials showing the date and month, respectively. When the clock is activated, music plays, the fountains on the musical box and on the terrace revolve, the figures move, and the boat sails. On the terrace, a man holds a ball out to a lion, which turns its head left and right. Under the palm tree, men with birds also revolve.

　　通体铜镀金，分三层。下层为乐箱，箱的正面似一小型舞台，内有布景、水法、人和盆花等。箱的台面中间有玻璃高台，高台上为双象驮钟，表盘中心是一秒针，上方为走时盘，下方左右是日历和月历盘。启动后，音乐奏起，底箱和高台内水法转动，人物活动，船只航行；高台前戏狮人举球，作戏狮动作，狮头左右摆动；棕榈树下的持鸟、持鹰人也随着转动。乐止，一切活动停止。

73

Gilded Copper Chiming Clock Set in a Mirror

Made about 1770, London
By William Hughes
61 x 40 x 21cm

铜镀金玻璃柱音乐镜表
约1770年
英国伦敦　威廉·休斯
（William Hughes）制造
61 × 40 × 21 厘米

This is a combination of a clock and a dressing table. Both the front and back of the musical box at the lower level have two drawers each for cosmetics and similar stuff. On top of the stand are four dancing figures, two holding flowers and two holding shields, around an oblong mirror. On the blue glass that sparkles at the back of the mirror is a small dial with hands to indicate the hours and minutes. It is wound up by a small key. The four corners of the musical box are each topped with a copper cup which was a popular decorative article for European clocks and watches at the time. On both sides of the mirror are square and pointed pillars carved out of transparent glass.

　　集钟表、妆台于一体。底层乐箱的前后两侧各有两个小抽屉，是放置梳妆用品的。底座上方雕有铜质四个舞人，两人持花环，两人持盾牌，围绕在一面椭圆形镜下。镜的背面莹莹闪光的蓝色玻璃中间嵌着一块小表，表盘有时针、秒针，用小钥匙上弦。在乐箱上的四角有四个铜质奖杯，这是当时欧洲钟表流行的饰件，镜子的两侧还竖立着透明玻璃雕刻的方尖柱，和其它饰件一起构成了和谐统一的整体。

British Clocks and Watches   英　国　钟　表

74

Gilded Copper Clock Supported by Four Goats and Two Angels

Made about 1770, London
By William Hughes
58.5 x 36 x 29.2cm

铜镀金四羊驮两人举表
约1770年
英国伦敦　威廉·休斯
(William Hughes)制造
58.5 × 36 × 29.2厘米

On the stand are four gilded copper goats supporting a two-story gilded copper box, the lower level of which is a musical box with an urban landscape painting on the front. The painting portrays a cheering crowd of people. Behind are the mechanical parts of the clock. The upper story is a gorgeously decorated box for cosmetics. In the center of the front part of the box is a portrait of a Greek goddess. At each of the four corners is a gilded pillar inlaid with glass. On the cover of the upper level of the box are two angels holding a two-hand dial in the shape of a flower vase. When the clock is activated, music plays, and the people in front of the urban landscape painting dance merrily.

　　钟底站立四只铜镀金山羊背负两层铜镀金箱,底层是乐箱,正面凹入部分以城市风景画作布景,画前有欢乐的人群,后部安置钟表机械。上层是装饰华丽的规矩箱,供放化妆用品用,箱前中央嵌有希腊神话故事中的人物画,箱的四角各有一根嵌玻璃的镀金柱,晶莹剔透。上层箱盖上有两个小天使抬着二针瓶式表。上弦启动后,音乐奏响,城市布景前的男女人群欢快的起舞。

75

Gilded Copper Chiming Pocket Watch with Openwork Enamel Decoration

Made about 1770, London
By William Hughes
16cm in diameter,
6cm thick

铜镀金镂花珐琅套音乐
怀表
约1770年
英国伦敦　威廉·休斯
(William Hughes)制造
直径16厘米　厚6厘米

The watch has a cover. The front of it has a glass cover inlaid with a circle of diamonds. Its back bears flower carvings. In the middle is an enamel painting of two girls and a dog. The dial consists of two parts. The top half is decorated with a little bridge with a man on it. Under the bridge is a fountain. The lower half has a two-hand dial. When the clock is activated, the man walks over the bridge and the fountain turns to create an impression of a turbulent river.

　　此怀表有一表套，前有一玻璃蒙，镶嵌着钻石圈口。背面雕有花叶，中间为描绘二少女对话的珐琅画。表盘一分为二，上半圆的饰景是一小桥，行人，桥下是一组水法似流水；下半圆是二针时分盘。表盘中心是秒针，周围标有秒数。开动机械，在乐曲中行人过桥，水法转动，似湍急的水流。

76
Calendar Clock with Hawksbill Turtle Shell Inlaid with Copper Patterns

Made in the 18th century, London
By William Hatt
61 x 32.2 x 22.5cm

玳瑁楼嵌铜饰日历钟
18世纪
英国伦敦 威廉·哈特
(William Hatt)制造
61 × 32.2 × 22.5厘米

英 国 钟 表 *British Clocks and Watches*

This tower hawksbill turtle shell clock is inlaid with gilded decorations The two-hand calendar dial has two small dials at its top, one for turning the music on and off and the other for changing the four tunes. Music plays as the clock strikes the hour.

　形似楼阁的玳瑁钟体上镶嵌着镀金纹饰。二针带日历盘，能走时、打时、打乐，显示日期。钟盘上方有两个小盘，一个为乐曲开关盘，一个是可调换四支乐曲的调换盘。

77
Gilded Copper Mirror Clock

Made about 1780, London
By Barbot
94 x 35 x 30cm

铜镀金反光镜滚球钟
约1780年
英国伦敦
巴博特 (Barbot) 制造
94 × 35 × 30厘米

British Clocks and Watches 英 国 钟 表

The gilded copper chest of the box is covered with a lacquer painting. The upper and lower doors have paintings of countryside scenery. On the back of the doors are portraits of ladies. When the doors are opened, one finds a mirror with twisting double rails. The curved legs on top of the chest support a two-hand clock with a dragon with a pointed tongue serving as the pendulum. When the clock is activated, a small copper ball enters the chest and rolls along the rails. Actually the rails are installed on a flat surface but the mirror creates a vertical image.

　　铜镀金箱式钟，箱面为油漆彩画。下部和上部两扇门上绘有乡村小景画，门的背面绘有仕女画。门内有一挡板，放平后通过反光镜，可以看到交错的双轨。箱上曲腿支架上有一二针时钟，钟下垂一舌尖似箭的翼龙为钟摆。启动后，一个小铜球进入箱内，沿着轨道上下滚动而不下坠。实际上滚球的装置是平放着的，只是利用斜面镜的反射，使之产生立体效果。

78
Gilded Copper Tower Clock Supported by Goats

Made about 1780, London
By Barbot
103 x 40 x 40cm

铜镀金四羊驮塔式转花钟
约1780年
英国伦敦
巴博特(Barbot)制造
103 × 40 × 40 厘米

英 国 钟 表 *British Clocks and Watches*

The clock has a stand of gilded copper, shaped like a hill. At each of the four corners of the stand is a soldier. A snake, lizard and turtle are found on the hill. In a cave are four ferocious lions. Also on the hill, four goats are with bent legs support the musical box, the front of which has nine spiraling flowers of red and white glass. On the top is a pavilion with a hero holding a star on his head. When the music starts, all the flowers begin spiraling, radiating dazzling colors.

钟为铜镀金山石形底座。底座四角站立着拿枪的勇士,石上爬着蛇、蜥蜴和乌龟等,在石洞内站着四条雄狮,山石上四只山羊驮着曲腿支架,支撑着乐箱。箱的正面有九朵红白玻璃料石的旋转花,表顶上有一小亭,亭顶蹲着一大力士,头顶宝星。启动后,在乐声中,所有的转花都在旋转,光彩流溢。

79
Gilded Copper Fountain Chiming Clock Supported by an Elephant

Made about 1780, London
By Barbot
110 x 48 x 40cm

铜镀金象驮水法塔乐钟
约1780年
英国伦敦
巴博特（Barbot）制造
110 × 48 × 40厘米

British Clocks and Watches 英 国 钟 表

The musical box at the bottom has a heavy frame of gilded copper. On the frame are birds and small animals. Inside the frame is a landscape painting at the front are movable figures. At the four corners of the box stand towering palm trees. On the box in the middle is a golden elephant carrying on its back a two-hand clock made of colorful glass and gemstones. On each side of the elephant is a sea lion spouting water to create a fountain. The tower has a three-story pagoda, with a different kind of fountain at each level. The top story is crowned with a sparkling star. When the clock is activated, the figures in front of the landscape painting move, the sea lions spout water and the fountains cascade like waterfalls. Meanwhile the star at the top turns.

　　底层的乐箱，用厚重的铜镀金为框，框上雕有家禽和小动物，框内有田园风光画，画前有活动的人物。在乐箱的四角有高高的棕榈树。乐箱上居中站立一只金色灿然的铜象背驮彩色玻璃料石镶圈口的二针时钟。象的左右各有一只口吐水法的海狮。钟上有塔三层，每层都有形式各异的水法。塔尖有光芒四射的宝星。启动后，画前的人物走动，海狮喷水，钟上的三层水法像瀑布流动，顶上星光转动，颇有意趣。

80
Gilded Copper Fountain Chiming Clock with Revolving Flowers

Made 1765-1790, London
By Benjamin Ward
88 x 38 x 38cm

铜镀金转花水法乐钟
约 1765 – 1790 年
英国伦敦
本杰明·沃德
(Benjamin Ward)制造
88 × 38 × 38 厘米

British Clocks and Watches 英 国 钟 表

The lower level is a square musical box carved with flowers and leaves. A painting of a thick forest is set deep in the front part of the box. In front of the painting is water with a sailboat. On the two sides of the musical box are landscape paintings featuring pastureland and countryside villas. On top of the box is a pavilion, the pillars of which are carved to resemble palm tree trunks. Inside the pavilion there is a small bridge over a river and a waterfall. Further up, curved legs support a two-hand clock. When the clock is activated, the waterfall flows, while the boat sails on the river.

　　此钟的造型简捷明快。底层为方形乐箱，周围雕饰以花叶纹，正面凹入的箱体背景绘有原始森林，画前的水法似流水，上有帆船行驶。乐箱左右两侧各为田园牧场和乡村别墅的风景画。台座上亭柱为棕榈树干造型，亭内有小桥流水，中间为帘状的水法。上层曲腿支架上，有一两针钟。当钟表启动后，水法转动似瀑布飞泻，帆船走动。

81

Gilded Copper and Enamel Vase Clock

Made in the 18th century, London
By Daniel Quare
43x19cm; dial 5.4cm in diameter

铜镀金珐琅壁瓶式表

18 世纪

英国伦敦

丹尼尔·夸尔

(Daniel Quare)制造

43 × 19 厘米

表直径 5.4 厘米

英　国　钟　表　British Clocks and Watches

This is a Chinese style vase inlaid with a clock. Such vases were often found standing by the sedan chairs of the emperor and empress and against walls in rooms. The clock can be opened in the front, with its mechanical parts hidden between two layers of boards. The mechanical system carries in English the name of Daniel Quare (1649-72). Quare was an early clock and watchmaker in Britain, who made outstanding contributions to this industry.

为中国式的壁瓶表。壁瓶常装饰在帝后的轿子和室内的墙壁上。表嵌于瓶腹上，从前边可打开表蒙，机芯在前后夹板之间，以发条、塔轮、链条为源动力，带动齿轮系统，为游丝摆轮。机芯后板上刻有丹尼尔·夸尔(1649－1726年)的英文字样，丹尼尔·夸尔是英国早期的钟表制造师，为英国钟表业做出了卓越的贡献。

82
Hawksbill Turtle Shell Tower Clock with Sailing Boat and Movable Figures

Made about 1780, London

By Edward Wicksteed

45 x 31 x 23cm

玳瑁楼式跑船跑人时乐钟

约1780年

英国伦敦

爱德华·维克斯梯

(Edward Wicksteed)制造

45 × 31 × 23 厘米

British Clocks and Watches 英 国 钟 表

This is a wooden clock inlaid with hawksbill turtle shell, and gilded copper and silver carved decorations. Four crouching lions serve as the legs of the clock. The two-hand dial is flanked by two smaller dials, one for turning the music on and off and the other for changing the four tunes. There are three winding holes on the dial for controlling the ticking, striking of the time and the music. Above the dial is a landscape painting, in front of which are movable figures and a boat. The clock has a domed roof like that of a church. Beneath the lower edge of the dome is a circular corridor, behind the arched gate of which are movable figures. When the clock is activated, the figures move and the boat sails to the accompaniment of four tunes one after the other.

此钟为木胎镶玳瑁、铜镀金和银雕花装饰，四只伏卧的雄狮为钟足，钟体内是机械装置，正面为二针钟盘，盘下方左右各有一小盘，一为乐曲启止盘，一为变换四支乐曲盘，表盘上有三个上弦孔，为打时、打乐、走时孔。表盘上方有一布景画，画前有人物、船只。顶端为教堂穹顶式，顶的下方环以一圈回廊，回廊的拱门内有行走的小人。启动后，小人行走，船只游动，同时奏乐，放完四套乐曲后，方停。

83

Black Lacquer Wooden Tower Table Clock with Copper Decorations

Made 1846-97, London
By John Bennett
122 x 74 x 37cm

黑漆木楼嵌铜饰大座钟
约 1846 – 1897 年
英国伦敦
约翰·班尼特
(John Bennett) 制造
122 × 74 × 37 厘米

英 国 钟 表 *British Clocks and Watches*

John Bennett was born into a clock manufacturer's family in Greenwich, London. His father died when he was still young. When he was 16 years old, he began to help his mother manage her business and later became the owner of a factory and a shop. He made his living by making and selling clocks and other timepieces. In 1872, he was made a lord by Queen Victoria. Some of his clocks were exported to China. This is one of them.

On the front of the clock is a two-hand dial. Above are three smaller dials. The one in the middle is to adjust the accuracy of the time, while the two smaller ones on the sides are for controlling striking, producing music and changing the tunes.

约翰·班尼特出生于英国伦敦格林威治一钟表制造商的家庭，父亲早亡，16 岁即帮助母亲经营生意，后来发展成拥有一个工厂和一个商店的老板，制造和出售钟表和标准计时仪。1862－1889 年担任地方议会议员，曾任伦敦行政司法长官。1872 年被维多利亚女王授予爵士称号。1897 年去世。他制造了许多钟表，曾销售到中国。这座钟是其中之一。

此钟能走时、打时、打乐。正面有一大表盘有时针、分针。其上有三个小表盘，正中是调快慢的针，两边的小盘分别是停打时，停打乐盘和更换乐曲的盘。

84

Gilded Copper Pavilion Globe Clock with Gemstone Decorations

Made 1771-1811, London
By Robert Philip
68 x 36 x 36cm

铜镀金亭式料石地球钟
约 1771 – 1811 年
英国伦敦
罗伯特·菲力普
(Robert Philip)制造
68 × 36 × 36 厘米

The frame of the gilded copper clock is inlaid with colorful gemstones. In the middle is a two-hand dial. Above are two smaller dials -- the one on the left for calendar display and the one on the right for stopping the striking. Between the two smaller dials is a globe made of blue and white gemstones. When the clock is activated, the globe revolves to reveal the white side during the day and the blue side during the night.

　　铜镀金镂花钟壳上嵌各色料石。正面为一二针时钟盘，盘的上方左右各有一小盘，左边小盘标示阴历日期，右边为停止打时盘。两个小盘中间是一白蓝两色料石制成的地球，当启动后，在机械的带动下，球体转动，白天显露白色的一面，晚间露出蓝色的一面，二十四小时自转一周。

85
Gilded Copper Pocket Watch with Gemstones Inlaid Around the Dial

Made 1779-1808, London
By Robert Ward
5cm in diameter

铜镀金镶料石圈口明机芯怀表
约 1779 – 1808 年
英国伦敦
罗伯特·沃德
(Robert Ward)制造
表径 5 厘米

英 国 钟 表　*British Clocks and Watches*

This gilded copper watch is inlaid with red and white gemstones around the dial. A keyhole for winding is visible on the white enamel dial. At the back the case has a glass cover through which the mechanical parts and the carved patterns along with the manufacture's name, "Robert Ward", can be clearly seen.

　　此表为铜镀金镶红白料石圈口，白珐琅表盘上方有上弦孔。表壳后盖安有玻璃表蒙，透过玻璃可以清晰地看到机芯和后板上雕刻的花纹，以及制造商的姓名"Robert Ward"。表的机芯以发条盒、塔轮、链条为源动力，带动齿轮系统。

86
Gilded Copper Clock with Boy and Sheep

Made 1779-1808, London
By Robert Ward
93 x 51 x 39cm

铜镀金少年牵羊钟
约 1779 – 1808 年
英国伦敦
罗伯特·沃德
(Robert Ward) 制造
93 × 51 × 39 厘米

British Clocks and Watches   英   国   钟   表

The stand of the clock is a musical box on which is a boy leading a sheep. The clock has one large and two small dials. The large dial has three hands for marking the seconds, minutes and hours. The small dial on the left is for changing the eight tunes, and the one on the right is for switching the music on and off. On the two sides of the musical box are landscape paintings covered with curtains that can be rolled up. The winding holes are at the back of the musical box. When the clock is activated, the curtain on the right side rolls up to reveal two roosters fighting. When the left curtain is rolled up, one sees galloping horses pulling a carriage. Each time the music plays, the curtain rises and falls three times, displaying three different scenes.

此钟底层为乐箱,箱上站着一牵羊少年,山羊毛和少年衣着的质感以及人物形象都十分逼真,显示了当时英国雕塑艺术的高超水平。正面嵌有一大二小三个表盘,中间大盘有时、分、秒针;左边是乐曲盘,可变换八支音乐;右边是乐曲的开关盘。箱的两侧有卷帘风景画,乐箱后有上弦孔。启动后,在乐声中,右边帘卷起,里边有二只公鸡相斗,背景画可以变换三次;左边帘卷起,里边有一辆车在奔驰,音乐每开动一次,帘子卷落三次,最后停止。

87
Wooden Tower Clock with Copper Decorations, Sailing Boat and Fountain

Made in the 18th century, London
By Thomas Macane
67 x 44 x 30cm

木楼嵌铜饰跑船水法钟
18 世纪
英国伦敦
托马斯·麦考尼
(Thomas Macane)制造
67 × 44 × 30 厘米

英 国 钟 表 *British Clocks and Watches*

The wooden frame is decorated with openwork gilded copper of sculpted flowers and figures, giving the timepiece an elegant and solemn look. In the center is a large dial with the name of the manufacturer, "Thomas Macane". There are two smaller dials above it -- the left one for controlling the music and the right one for changing the seven tunes. The music control system is at the back of the clock. Under a roller are 14 bells in a row. Eleven of them are struck by two hammers each and three by one hammer each. When the roller turns, copper nails pluck at the hammer handles and make them strike the bells. In the indented space above the dial are a sailing boat and a fountain, which are activated when the string on the right is pulled. When this happens, the fountain seems to surge with waves, and the boat moves forward.

木质的钟壳上嵌有铜镀金镂雕花卉人物装饰，典雅庄重。正面为二针钟盘，能走时、打时、打乐，钟盘上写有制造商的名字"Thomas Macane"。钟盘上方左右各有一小盘，左边有奏乐、止乐功能，右边的有换乐曲功能。共有七支乐曲。控制乐曲的机械装置在钟背面，有一铜制的滚筒，根据七支乐曲的音阶在筒上置铜钉，铜钉距离有疏有密。在滚筒的下面平列 14 个钟碗，其中有 11 个钟碗上有双锤，3 个钟碗是单锤，共 25 个锤。当齿轮带动滚筒转动时，滚筒上的铜钉，拨动锤柄，锤击钟碗，因钟碗大小不同，发出的音阶也不同，即奏出动听的乐曲，钟盘上方的布景内有航船和水法，只须轻拉右边的绳便能启动，水法似水波浪前进，船只向前驰行。

88
Gilded Copper Tower Four-sided Clock

Made in the 18th century, London
By Delul
44.2 x 24 x 24 cm

铜镀金楼式规矩箱四面钟
18世纪
英国伦敦
德鲁尔(Delul)制造
44.2 × 24 × 24厘米

British Clocks and Watches   英 国 钟 表

This three-story tower clock was made by applying agate and thin metal slabs to a wooden frame. It was then wrapped with an exquisite gilded copper cover with openwork patterns. In the middle of the lower story are two doors which, when opened, reveal drawers at three levels containing a telescope, a reflector, a dressing mirror, a knife, a cosmetic box and perfume. The middle story is the musical box, and the top story contains three mechanisms for controlling the striking of the time and the playing of music. The control switches are located in the middle story.

钟体为三层楼阁式，木质钟壳外镶嵌玛瑙和青石薄片，外层为精致的铜镀金镂空花罩。底层中间有两扇小门，打开后露出三层抽屉，抽屉里放置着望远镜、反光镜、梳妆镜、小刀、粉盒、香水等物件。中层为乐箱。上层四面为表盘，机芯共三套装置，可打时、走时、打乐，开关在中层。

89
Gilded Copper Pearl-inlaid Pocket Watch

Made 1757-1772, London
By Charles Cabrier
8.8cm high, 5.2cm between the opposite angles

铜镀金镶珠石杯式表
1757－1772年
英国伦敦
查尔斯·卡布雷
(Charles Cabrier)制造
高8.8厘米
对角径5.2厘米
口径4.3厘米

The green enamel octagonal case is cup-shaped and has gilded copper flower decorations. The cover is inlaid with pearls and precious stones. The diameter of the cup opening is 3.2 cm. The dial bears the inscription "Charles Cabrier, London". Its delicate and exquisite features make it an unusual masterpiece.

　　表壳为绿珐琅八角带盖杯，上镶铜镀金镂花装饰，盖镶珍珠和宝石，杯口直径3.2厘米，二针表，表盘上有署名"Charles Cabrier"和"London"。此表精致华丽，是一件不可多得的佳品。

90
Gilded Copper Chariot Chiming Clock Pulled by an Elephant

Made around 1780, Britain
136cm long, 72cm high

铜镀金象拉战车乐钟
约1780年左右
英国制造
车长136厘米
高72厘米

British Clocks and Watches 英 国 钟 表

This is the longest Western clock kept in the Forbidden City. Mechanism installed in the belly of the elephant controls its trunk, ears, eyes and tail. Under the belly is a wheel that controls the direction of the elephant. In front of the chariot is a gilded copper bucket supported by two wheels. Inside the bucket is a large spring which enables the elephant to move forward, pulling the chariot. Behind the bucket is a small box containing a spring which enables the rider to look left and right from the box. At the back of the chariot is a square musical box fixed to two wheels. On the two sides of the box are landscape paintings. On the box are two soldiers holding a double-sided dial. There are four sets of springs that control different parts of the chariot, enabling it to move forward. When music plays, the elephant blinks its eyes, flaps its ears, stretches out or rolls up its trunk and wags its tail.

这是清宫收藏的最长的西洋钟。象腹内有一盘发条机械，控制着象鼻、眼、耳、尾。腹下还有一个控制大象行走方向的轮子，战车前部有一个铜镀金筒，筒下有两轮，筒内装有一盘发条，是大象行走，带动车厢及开动战车的主要动力源。筒后有一小方箱，内装置一盘发条，可使站立箱上的指挥官左右转动眺望。车的后方是一个方形乐箱，下有两轮，箱的两侧有风景画，箱上两士兵围两面钟。这辆战车共有四盘发条，各部分协调动作，所以战车才能正常行驶。在音乐声中，大象能眨眼，煽动耳朵，卷伸鼻子，摆动尾巴，形象十分逼真。战车轮子呈弧形走动，将士们精神抖擞，显现出胜利者的神态。

91
Gilded Copper Clock Supported by an Elephant

Made in the 18th century, Britain
129 x 50 x 36cm

铜镀金象驮琵琶摆钟
18 世纪
英国制造
129 × 50 × 36 厘米

British Clocks and Watches　英　国　钟　表

The stand of the clock rests on four copper lions. The lower level is a two-story musical box. On the surface, the doors are painted with forestry scenery. On the musical box stands a copper elephant, whose ears, eyes and trunk can move. On the elephant's back is a ring in the shape of a pipa, a traditional Chinese musical instrument. The ring is beautifully inlaid with decorative stones. A two-hand dial hangs in the middle. The dial is marked with the minutes, hours, calendar and the 24 lunar terms. When the clock strikes the time, the door at the lower level automatically opens to reveal a scene of a man rowing a boat on a small river. The door above it opens to reveal a church structure. At the same time, the eyes, trunk and tail of the elephant move, as do flowers made of gemstones.

　　钟足为四只铜铸狮子。底层为乐箱，正面是二层门，门外绘有树林风景。乐箱上站着一只铜镀金象，眼、耳、鼻都能活动自如。象背上驮着嵌料石的琵琶形环，环间挂二针钟，在钟盘上弦，能报时，钟盘指示有时、分格，还有日历、朔望日。机芯以发条、塔轮、链条为动力源，带动齿轮传动系统，报时或启动时，第一层门自动开启，内现人在溪中泛舟的图景，第二层门内有一教堂式建筑。同时象的眼、鼻、尾都在活动，料石制的花朵也在转动。

92
Gilded Copper Orchestra and Mirror Clock

Made in the 18th century, Britain
124 x 69 x 38cm

铜镀金人奏乐容镜钟
18世纪
英国制造
124 × 69 × 38厘米

British Clocks and Watches 英 国 钟 表

This clock consists of two stories. The lower one has fountain decorations on both sides. In front of the fountains are openwork sculpture block prints on copper portraying birds returning to their nests in the forest. The front part carries a landscape painting. When the clock is activated, an elephant carrying a vase emerges from behind a door and a man offers treasures. In the center is a three-hand dial with stone flowers fixed to its edge. On the left and right and above are five small gilded copper figures each holding two hammers in their hands. In front of each are two bells. In the background is a screen which supports an elegant oblong mirror.

When the clock is fully wound, the five figures move left and right, and strike the bells to produce a tune. The fountain plays and pineapple flowers revolve at the same time.

钟分为上下两层。下层箱面两侧有水法，水法前镂雕鸟归林景象铜板画，正中门内嵌有着绘有乡野风光的风景画，当机械启动后门内有象驮瓶，献宝人出入。箱上正中置周边镶有料石花的三针时钟，钟的左和右和上方有五个双手执锤的铜镀金小人，每人身前都有两个钟碗。其后有一屏风，支托着一面装饰华美的椭圆形的镜子。

上弦后，五个人左右转动，敲打钟碗，演奏出悦耳美的乐曲，水法上下流动闪闪发光，上层两侧的菠萝花也同时旋转。钟上容镜可用作梳妆照容。

93
Gilded Copper Movable Pagoda Clock

Made in 1780, Britain
105 x 39 x 39cm

铜镀金转人升降塔钟
1780 年
英国制造
105 × 39 × 39 厘米

British Clocks and Watches 英 国 钟 表

The clock's stand is a square musical box, the front and two sides of which all carry dials. The dial in the front has an extra hand for seconds. On top of the stand is a pentagonal gilded copper pagoda, the eaves of which are hung with bells. The body and tiles of the pagoda are inlaid with colorful stones. When the clock is activated, the musical box plays traditional Chinese folk tunes, and the top of the pagoda rises, followed by the second, third and fourth levels. When the next hour arrives, the pagoda collapses, story by story, with the eaves folding into two layers at the fifth story. At the same time, the copper figures on the four corners revolve. The lower section of the pagoda has a fountain behind the door in the middle.

The rise and collapse of the pagoda are controlled by a spring, which activates an ingenious chain-and-pulley system.

钟座为正方形乐箱。乐箱的正面和两侧都有钟盘, 只有正面盘上有秒针。箱上层立圆柱形五层铜镀金塔, 塔檐悬挂铜铃。塔身和瓦陇嵌有各色料石。启动后, 乐箱内发出悦耳的中国民间乐曲, 塔顶升起, 二、三、四层也依次上升。到了下一钟点时, 塔身逐层下降, 塔檐重叠于第五层檐。最下层塔身中间门内水法转动, 四角站立的四铜人也旋转。

塔的升降是由塔内一直通塔尖的方梃子控制的。乐箱内有一盘发条做为动力, 方梃子用铁链拉着, 塔升起时, 利用发条的力量, 带动里面的一个滑车, 滑车绞着铁链子, 梃子上升; 下降时, 利用塔身的坠力, 并借助发条的阻力作用, 使滑车缓缓往下放梃子, 否则升时力不足, 下降时则易坠落。这种装置, 反映了工匠们的智慧和才能。

94

Gilded Copper Umbrella Clock with Revolving Flowers

Made in the 18th century, Britain
83 x 24 x 24cm

铜镀金转花翻伞钟
18 世纪
英国制造
83 × 24 × 24 厘米

The gilded copper and enamel frame used for this clock is extremely rare among clocks made in Britain. The lower story of this clock, which is in the form of a two-story tower, is a musical box. In the front part is a round double-layer decoration of green, yellow and white gemstones. In the middle of the second story is a three-hand dial. The tower is crowned with an enamel umbrella supporting a bouquet of flowers made of gemstones. When the clock strikes, the umbrella opens to reveal the fountain hidden inside. Meanwhile the flower on top of the umbrella revolves, as do the three spiraling flowers on the side. When the music stops, the umbrella folds up and the flower covering the fountain stops revolving. The picture shows the clock's decorations when it is activated.

此钟所用的铜镀金珐琅钟壳，在英国钟表中是极少见的。钟为二层楼阁式，底层为乐箱，正面为一圆形红、白、黄、绿多色双层料石花。第二层正中为三针时钟，顶端为珐琅伞，伞顶有一束嵌料石花。钟有三盘发条为动力源。当报时，或单独启动玩意时，楼顶伞撑开，露出里边的水法，伞顶花束转动，侧面三朵螺旋花自转；乐止，伞渐收拢，覆盖水法，转花也就停止转动。此图为启动时形状。

95
Gilded Copper Fountain Clock

Made in the 18th century, Britain
103 x 50 x 45cm

铜镀金水法连机动大座钟
18世纪
英国制造
103 × 50 × 45厘米

British Clocks and Watches 英 国 钟 表

TThis clock has two stories. The lower one is a musical box with drawers inlaid with red and white gemstones. The mechanical parts are hidden in the drawers. On each of the four corners of the box is a spiral flower made of gemstones, which can revolve.

The body of the clock is suspended on a frame. It has three hands, and strikes every hour. When fully wound, it can keep working for seven days. The fountain and flower on the top of the frame revolve to the accompaniment of music.

分上下两层，下层乐箱，前有嵌红、白料石花抽屉，内装有钟表机械。上层四角各有一嵌料石的螺旋花，可以转动。

钟体用铜梃子悬挂在架上，可以摆动，表盘上有时、分、秒针，走时一圈为24小时，每小时打点。上满弦后，可以走七天，架顶上的水法柱、螺旋花可伴随着音乐转动。

96

Gilded Copper Clock Decorated with Revolving Flowers in a Vase

Made in the 18th century, Britain
83x28x19cm

铜镀金花瓶式顶转花钟
18 世纪
英国制造
83 × 28 × 19 厘米

The stand, which also serves as a musical box, is inlaid with colorful gemstones. Below is a three-hand dial. The clock is crowned with an enamel vase holding a bouquet of flowers made of gemstones and leaves of gilded copper.

When the clock is activated, music plays, and the flower pattern above the dial turns around and changes color among green, red, white and yellow. At the same time, the flower at the top revolves, while opening and closing.

钟底座为乐箱，箱前镶有各色料石，下有三针时钟，钟上是一朵料石变色转花。箱顶一珐琅花瓶中插一束花，以料石为花，铜镀金的枝叶。

启动后，钟盘上方的变色花转动，并变换白、黄、红、绿四种颜色，瓶中的花束转动，侧面花朵自转并随梃转动，中心花朵一开一合，乐箱奏乐曲。

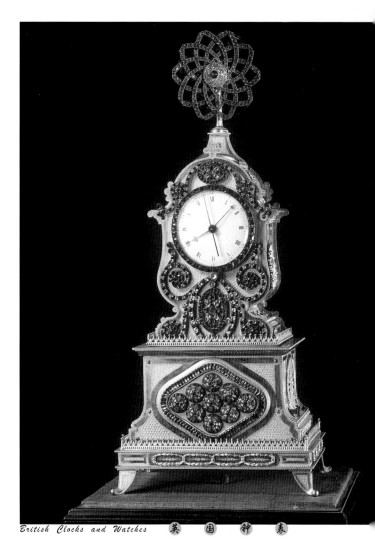

97
Gilded Copper Flower Revolving Clock

Made in the 18th century, Britain
49 x 22 x 16 cm

铜镀金转花钟
18世纪
英国制造
49 × 22 × 16 厘米

British Clocks and Watches   英   国   钟   表

The body of this clock is decorated with revolving flowers made of colorful gemstones. When the clock is activated, all the flowers revolve to the accompaniment of music. The blue and red flowers at the top revolve to the left and right interchangeably.

钟体由众多色彩艳丽的料石制作的旋转花为装饰物。启动后，花朵都能各自旋转；顶端红、蓝两色花则向左、右方向交错旋转，变幻出神奇的色彩；底座中发出美妙的音乐声。

98
Gilded Copper Rising and Falling Pavilion Clock Inlaid with Gemstones

Made in the 18th century, Britain
126 x 28 x 28 cm

铜镀金嵌料石升降塔钟
18世纪
英国制造
126 × 28 × 28 厘米

At the lower level is an octagonal musical box, which is also contains the mechanical parts. The front and the two sides of the clock are furnished with dials. The nine-story octagonal pagoda has bells hanging on the eaves. The pagoda's body is inlaid with blue stones. Every three hours, the pagoda completes a round of rising and falling. The pagoda can also revolve too. When this happens, the bells produce a jingling sound. The pagoda can also be made to rise and fall separately from the clock function.

底层为八角形乐箱，箱内有机械装置。箱的正面和两侧有钟盘。九层八角塔檐挂着响铃，塔檐镶有蓝色料石，与金色灿然的塔身相辉映。上弦后，可以报时，每三小时塔升、降一次，塔身可转动，塔铃随之叮当作响。塔身也可以单独启动升降。

99
Gilded Copper Clock Decorated with Three Children Striking the Hours

Made in the 18th century, Britain
77.5 x 35 x 20cm

铜镀金三人打乐钟
18世纪
英国制造
77.5 × 35 × 20厘米

British Clocks and Watches　英　国　钟　表

The lower story of the clock is decorated with meticulously carved elegant patterns, and has a three-hand dial, encircled by sparkling colorful gemstones. On the clock stand are three figures of kneeling children, which strike bells to mark the hours. They are surrounded by openwork revolving golden flowers. Behind them is a gilded copper screen decorated with carvings of Chinese wisteria. In the middle of the screen is a set of flower patterns inlaid with colorful gemstones. When the clock is activated, the eight flowers made of red and white gemstones at the top of the clock revolve accompanied by music, and the children strike their bells.

　　下层钟座雕有精致的纹饰，正面嵌一三针时钟，钟盘周围镶嵌着光芒四射的彩色料石。上层钟座上雕有三位形象生动跪着敲钟碗的儿童。三个钟碗被镂空的金色转花所遮掩。儿童背部围绕雕镂的铜镀金花藤萝屏风，屏风中央有一组彩色料石镶嵌的花饰。当钟启动后，顶端八朵红白料石镶成的团花随乐声转动，儿童敲打钟碗。

100
Gilded Copper
Partridge Clock
Made in the 18th
century, Britain
42 x 27 x 43 cm

铜镀金乐箱鹧鸪钟
18世纪
英国制造
42 × 27 × 43厘米

The four sides of the gilded copper rectangular musical box bear six colorful enamel paintings of women, with two European countryside scenery paintings and bas relief sculptures of birds and flowers on the two sides. On top of the musical box is a clock, behind which is a gilded copper partridge.

When the clock is activated, the partridge chirps to tell the time, while moving its head and tail.

　　铜镀金长方形的乐箱四壁,镶嵌着六幅颜色鲜艳的珐琅仕女画,其两旁饰有欧洲风格的乡村风景和花鸟浮雕。乐箱上前方有一座钟,钟后站立着一铜镀金鹧鸪。

　　当钟表启动后,鹧鸪发出咕咕声报时时,其头部和翅膀随之活动。

101
Gilded Copper Pavilion Clock with Rolling Balls, Swimming Ducks and a Fountain

Made about 1775, Britain
130 x 53 x 45cm

铜镀金亭式滚球转鸭水法钟
约1775年
英国制造
130 × 53 × 45 厘米

JThe lower level is a musical box, which also contains the mechanical parts. The front and sides of the box are decorated with landscape paintings, including fountains. Above is a gilded three-story copper pagoda. At each story, the eaves are in the form of a dragon playing with a ball, and hung with bells. The pillars of the pagoda are entwined with leaves made of green gemstones. On the first story the floor is of glass to symbolize a pool, on which there are ducks. In the center of this story is a fountain. At the second story, there is a spiral staircase, under which is a snake with its mouth wide open. At the top story is a two-hand dial.

When the clock is activated, the fountain turns into a waterfall, and the flowers on all the stories automatically revolve. The ducks swim on the pond. Two balls roll down the spiral staircase at the second story into the mouth of the snake, and then they roll back up again.

底层是乐箱，内有机械。箱的正面和左右两侧风景画中有水法。乐箱上部是一铜镀金亭子，共三层，每层亭子檐头饰有翼龙戏珠和挂铃，亭子的立柱缠绕着嵌绿色料石的叶子。下层亭内以玻璃面作池塘，塘中有鸭子，四角雕有站立的玩鹰人，中间为水法立柱；二层亭内水法柱上盘梯围绕，梯下是一条张口的盘蛇；第三层亭中有一二针时钟。

钟启动后，在清脆悦耳的乐曲声中，水法柱转动犹瀑布，各层缠花柱也同时旋转，鸭子在池塘内浮游；第二层亭子内的盘梯上两个小球沿梯而下，落入蛇口内，然后盘旋而下至出口处，再落入盘梯，循环往复，颇有奇趣。

英　国　钟　表　　　British Clocks and Watches

102
Gilded Copper Clock Supported by a Camel and Decorated with Revolving Figures

Made about 1780, Britain
82 x 51 x 28cm

铜镀金水法转人骆驼驮
钟
约1780年
英国制造
82 × 51 × 28厘米

British Clocks and Watches 英 国 钟 表

The musical box is decorated on its edges with carved grass and leaf patterns. In the center is a lacquer landscape painting. In front of the painting is a bridge and a boat, while on the left and right are trees and a fountain. The two sides of the musical box also bear lacquer landscape paintings with figures in the front. On top of the musical box are exquisitely carved and cast gilded copper birds, butterflies and bushes, in addition to a huge camel carrying on its back a gilded copper European-style tower, the walls of which are inlaid with enamel portraits of women. On the front there is a calendar and a three-hand dial.

When the clock is activated, music plays, and the fountain creates an image of flowing water. The boat, figures and carriage all seem to be moving forward, while birds and butterflies flap their wings as if about to take flight.

　　底层乐箱的四周雕有草叶纹的装饰，正面中央绘有田园风景的漆画，画前有桥、船等，左右为树木和水法。箱的两侧也为乡村田园风光的漆画。画面上也有人物等。乐箱上为雕铸精妙的铜镀金小鸟、蝴蝶和树丛，以及一头高大的骆驼驮着一座铜镀金的欧式楼阁，楼的正面墙上嵌有珐琅女像，上方嵌有带日历的三针钟。

　　启动后，音乐响起，钟底层布景画前水法似流水，船只、人物、车都在行进，小鸟和蝴堞展翅欲飞。

103
Gilded Copper Clock Supported by Horses and Decorated with Revolving Figures, Flowers and Fountain

Made in the 18th century, Britain
127 x 55.5 x 55.5cm

铜镀金四马驮转花转人
水法钟
18世纪
英国制造
127 × 55.5 × 55.5厘米

British Clocks and Watches 英 国 钟 表

The four gilded corners of the clock stand rest on four gilded galloping horses. The first story is a musical box decorated with paintings of scenery. The front and back are decorated with paintings portraying scenery typical of European towns. In front of the paintings are small figures. The left and right sides are decorated with fountains. The musical box is surrounded with carved railings. On the box are four lions carrying a frame engraved with flower and leaf patterns, which support a two-hand dial with a small plate for indicating the seconds. In the center of the frame is a fountain surrounded by dancing men and women, and cranes.

When the clock is activated, the fountain seems to cascade like a waterfall. The flower on top of the dial revolves, the small figures begin walking, and the boat seems to glide along the surface of a river.

钟体的四角之下是四匹奋蹄前奔的铜马，通体镀金。底层为乐箱，箱的四面有布景，前后两面是欧洲城镇风俗画，画前置有小人；左右两面有水法。箱上四周以雕花栏杆为装饰，箱上四只狮子驮着花叶纹的架子，上有二针时钟，并有一个走秒的小盘。中间为一股水法，另有作舞蹈状的男女、引颈展翅的仙鹤等，皆为铜质镀金。

启动后，水法似瀑布倾泄而下，钟顶花朵转动，布景内小人走动，船只航行。乐止，一切活动停止。

104
Gilded Copper Figure Striking Bell Clock

Made in the 18th century, Britain
49 x 18 x 12cm

铜镀金转花人打钟
18 世纪
英国制造
49 × 18 × 12 厘米

British Clocks and Watches　英　国　钟　表

In the oblong cave at the front of the clock stand is a figure holding hammers ready to strike two bells. On the stand is a three-hand dial topped with a revolving flower. When the clock is activated, the stone flower on the stand turns, and the figure raises both hands to strike the bells.

钟座内有机械装置。座前椭圆形框洞内立一铜制的持锤报时人，其旁有两个钟碗。座上有三针时钟，其顶端有转花。钟表启动后，钟座上的料石花旋转，铜人的两手举起，敲打钟碗报时。

105
Wood-framed Iron Mechanical Clock

Made in the 18th century, Britain
42.8 x 27.5 x 16.5cm

木壳铁板机器钟
18 世纪
英国制造
42.8 × 27.5 × 16.5厘米

英　国　钟　表　*British Clocks and Watches*

The mechanical structure of this clock is similar to that of most clocks made in the same period. All the mechanical parts are made of iron, which when polished do not go rusty. The two ears on the side make it easy to move the clock.

此钟外形简洁，机械构造与同期钟相同，即以发条盒、塔轮、链条为动力的齿轮传动系统，所有机械零件都是铁制的，铁经过抛光不生锈。钟的两侧有环，可以自由搬动。

106
Gilded Copper, Agate-inlaid Telescope Clock

Made in the 18th century, Britain 10cm long, 4cm in diameter and 1.9cm in dial diameter

铜镀金饰玛瑙望远镜表
18世纪
英国制造
长10厘米　径宽4厘米
表径1.9厘米

British Clocks and Watches 英 国 钟 表

The entire body is of red agate decorated with flower and leaf patterns of gilded copper. The clock is inlaid in the center of the cover of the telescope. With the cover removed, the device serves as a telescope.

通体为红玛瑙质，外饰铜镀金雕花叶纹。表嵌在望远镜镜盖中心，镶玻璃料石口。取下盖，即为一单筒可调试望远镜。

107
**Silver Organ Clock
with Openwork
Sculpture**

*Made in the 18th
century, Britain
88 x 50 x 41cm*

银镂空花卉跑人风琴钟
*18 世纪
英国制造
88 × 50 × 41 厘米*

英　国　钟　表　*British Clocks and Watches*

The silver frame of this clock bears openwork figures and flowers. At the front is a spacious hall, in the center of which is a two-hand dial. Its pendulum is on the outside. The dial has a list of the days on the lower part and a list of the weeks on the upper part. On the left and right are musical dials. Below is a set of bas-relief figures, including angels. The top of the clock is decorated with 13 prize cups.

Apart from marking the time, the clock also can produce melodious organ tunes.

　　银质钟壳，镂雕人物和花卉等，正面构图为一深邃轩敞大厅，厅内正中嵌一二针时钟，明摆，下边有日历，上边有周历，左右为乐盘。钟盘下有一组浮雕人物，有演奏弹唱的、有扛旗的，还有带翅膀的小天使。顶部饰以十三个奖杯。

　　此钟除走时外，还能奏出悦耳的风琴乐曲。

108
Gilded Copper Framed Clock

Made in the 19th century, Britain
47cm high

铜镀金架挂钟
19世纪
英国制造
高47厘米

British Clocks and Watches　英　国　钟　表

From the gilded copper frame is suspended a three-hand clock. The clock strikes every hour.

铜镀金架的线条简洁流畅，钟悬挂于架上，钟盘上有时、分、秒针。上弦后，表机摆动，每小时报一次时。

109
Gilded Copper Clock Inlaid with Enamel Strips

Made in the 18th century, Britain
42 x 25 x 16cm

铜镀金嵌珐琅片钟
18 世纪
英国制造
42 × 25 × 16 厘米

This gilded copper clock has a two-hand dial. The lower part of the clock's dial is inlaid with blue enamel strips. When fully wound, it can keep working for 24 hours.

铜镀金质，二针时钟。钟盘下部嵌有蓝色珐琅片。以发条、塔轮、链条为动力源，带动齿轮，可走时报时。上弦后，可走二十四小时。

110
Mahogany Tower Clock Inlaid with Copper Strips

Made in the 18th century, Britain
55.5 x 39.5 x 25cm

红木楼式嵌铜饰三套钟
18 世纪
英国制造
55.5 × 39.5 × 25 厘米

British Clocks and Watches 英 国 钟 表

The mahogany stand of this clock is decorated with patterns of flowers in gilded copper strips. The two-hand dial is in white enamel. There are two smaller dials for striking the time and controlling the music.

　　红木楼式的钟座表面嵌有铜镀金花卉纹样。二针白磁钟盘，钟可走时、打时。钟盘上方有两个小盘，一为止乐，一为打乐。

111
Gilded Copper Clock Supported by Winged Animals with Flowers and a Fountain

Made in the 18th century, Britain
79 x 31 x 31cm

铜镀金变花水法翼兽驮钟
18世纪
英国制造
79 × 31 × 31 厘米

英 国 钟 表 *British Clocks and Watches*

The stand of the clock also serves as a musical box, the front of which is decorated with colorful flowers made of gemstones. At each of the four corners of the box is a winged animal supporting a three-hand clock. Below the dial is a fountain.

When the clock is activated, the flowers change color, and the fountain plays, to the accompaniment of music.

此钟底座是乐箱。箱的正面有各色料石嵌成的变色花和花卉。箱上四角各有一翼兽背负钟架，架上置一三针时钟，钟下有一束水法。

启动后，在乐曲声中，花变四种颜色转动，水法如喷泉一样倾泄。

112
Gilded Copper Clock with Automatic Doors

Made in the 18th century, Britain
125 x 77 x 44.5cm

铜镀金自开门人打钟
18世纪
英国制造
125 × 77 × 44.5厘米

British Clocks and Watches 英 国 钟 表

This clock consists of three levels. The mechanism is in the lower level, which also has four drawers for storing things. The middle level has automatic doors which open to reveal a small gilded copper figure whose job is to strike eight bells. Behind him and on the backs of the doors are revolving flowers made of colorful gemstones. The top level has a three-hand clock. When fully wound, the clock can keep working for seven days.

When the clock is activated, the middle-level doors open, and the figure begins to strike the bells to produce music. When the tune finishes, the doors shut automatically. The performance is conducted once every hour.

钟分三层，下层机械装置前有四个抽屉，放一些物件；中层自开门内有一铜镀金小人敲打钟碗奏乐，钟碗共八个，小人背后和门的背面嵌有各色料石转花；上层有一三针时钟，上一次弦可走七天。

启动后，中层门自动打开，门内的小人即开始击钟碗奏乐，奏完一曲后，门自动关上。每隔一小时演奏一次。

113
Hawksbill Turtle Shell Chiming Clock Inlaid with Copper Decorations

Made in the 18th century, Britain
39 x 19 x 12cm

玳瑁楼式嵌铜饰乐钟
18 世纪
英国制造
39 × 19 × 12 厘米

British Clocks and Watches 英 国 钟 表

The clock stand is made of hawksbill turtle shell, an expensive decorative material.

The clock has a two-hand dial flanked in the lower part by two smaller dials, respectively for turning the music on and off and changing the four tunes. Above the dial is a three-dimensional oil painting, in front of which are movable figures.

玳瑁是一种形如海龟的爬行动物，其甲壳是珍贵的装饰材料，此钟的钟座即是用这种材料制成的。

正面为二针时钟，钟盘下方左右各有一小盘，一是乐曲开关盘，一是调换四支乐曲盘。钟盘上方有立体油画布景，布景前有活动人物。

114
Gilded Copper Pocket Watch Inlaid with Diamonds

Made in the 19th century, Britain
6.6cm in diameter,
1cm thick

铜镀金珐琅镶钻石壳怀表
19世纪
英国制造
表径6.6厘米　厚1厘米

英　国　钟　表　*British Clocks and Watches*

The gilded copper watch case is decorated with blue enamel on the back and inlaid with a star-shaped diamond surrounded with eight plum flowers. The three-hand watch shows exquisite workmanship. The key attached to the watch is also meticulously produced in the same decorative style as the watch case.

　　三针表，铜镀金珐琅表壳，壳的背面蓝色珐琅镶有钻石宝星花，周围有八朵梅花，做工十分精致。表上所附的钥匙也十分讲究，其装饰风格与表壳一致。

115

Gilded Copper Clock with Strikers on Three Sides

Made in the 18th century, Britain
93 x 52 x 42cm

铜镀金转水法三面人打钟
18世纪
英国制造
93 × 52 × 42 厘米

British Clocks and Watches 英 国 钟 表

This clock consists of three stories. The lower story, which contains the mechanism, has three drawers in the front. Above the drawers is a rural landscape painting, in front of which are movable figures flanked by fountains. At the second story there are two small figures which strike a bell between them, with two other bells each on their left and right sides. Their heads and arms are movable. The four corners of the second story are decorated with revolving stone flowers. Four crouching camels support a gilded basin for receiving water coming out of a horse's mouth on the terrace of the third story. The pavilion also houses a fountain, the water from which flows round ribbons of stones. On the terrace of the third story are four horse tamers with their animals. In the center is a four-hand clock for indicating the seconds, minutes, hours and days.

The clock strikes the quarters and hours, while the figures on the second story beat the bells and shake their heads. The figures in front of the stage start to move, and the fountain and flower vase revolve.

钟体分为三层，下层装有机械零件，正面有三个抽屉，可以放置物品，其上有农村风景画，画前有可活动的人，两侧有水法；第二层台面正中和两侧各立两个击钟碗奏乐的小人，手臂和头部都能活动，四角还有嵌料石转花，四只卧驼背驮镀金盆，承接着从三层平台马口中流出的水法，亭子中间有缠绕料石花带的水法柱；第三层台面上立有四个驯马人及马，中央是一个四针时钟，有时、分、秒和日历针。

上弦后，钟可走时、报时、报刻，同时台面上的敲钟人手击钟、转头，舞台前的人物活动、水法柱、瓶花转动，音响和人物动作和谐，气氛非常热烈。

116
Gilded Copper Pocket Watch Decorated with Ladies Listening to Flute Playing

Made in the 19th century, Britain
6cm in diameter,
1.6cm thick

铜镀金珐琅听箫图壳怀表
19世纪
英国制造
表直径6厘米
厚1.6厘米

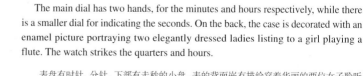
British Clocks and Watches 英 国 钟 表

The main dial has two hands, for the minutes and hours respectively, while there is a smaller dial for indicating the seconds. On the back, the case is decorated with an enamel picture portraying two elegantly dressed ladies listing to a girl playing a flute. The watch strikes the quarters and hours.

表盘有时针、分针，下部有走秒的小盘。表的背面嵌有描绘着华丽的两位女子聆听一位小女孩吹箫的珐琅画。摁一下表把，表可打簧报时、报刻，所以又叫问表。

117
Gilded Copper Pocket Watch Inlaid with Pearls

Made in the 18th century, Britain 5.5cm in diameter, 1cm thick

铜镀金嵌珐琅画镶珠怀表
18世纪
英国制造
表径5.5厘米　厚1厘米

英　国　钟　表　*British Clocks and Watches*

The front of the dial has three hands, indicating the seconds, minutes and hours respectively. Its circumference is inlaid with 50 pearls. The back is inlaid with 54 pearls surrounding an enamel picture.

铜镀金表壳，表的正面有时、分、秒针，周围一圈镶珍珠50粒。表的背面周围也嵌珍珠54粒，中间嵌珐琅画，画面清晰美丽，是一件精致的怀表。

118

Gilded Copper Pocket Watch with Copper Colored Dial Plate

Made in the 18th century, in Britain 5.5cm in diameter, 2cm thick

铜镀金铜色表盘怀表
18世纪
英国克莱（Clay）制造
表直径5.5厘米
厚2厘米

British Clocks and Watches 英 国 钟 表

This two-hand watch is complemented by an exquisitely made chain and key. When fully wound, a golden dragon moves in a forest on the back of the watch.

此表盘有时针和秒针，并附精美的链条和钥匙。上弦后走动，机芯背后有金龙在树林中游动。

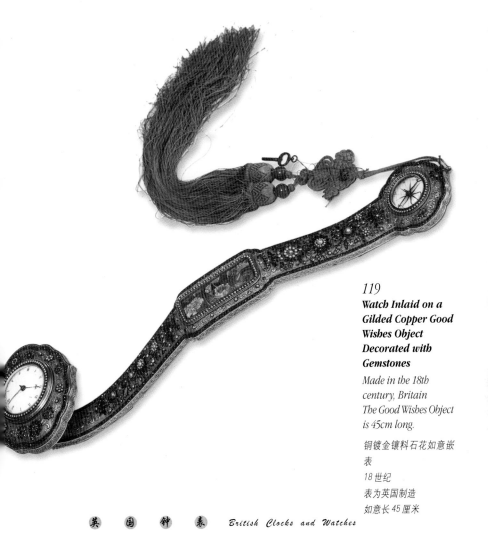

119
Watch Inlaid on a Gilded Copper Good Wishes Object Decorated with Gemstones

Made in the 18th century, Britain
The Good Wishes Object is 45cm long.

铜镀金镶料石花如意嵌表
18 世纪
表为英国制造
如意长 45 厘米

英　国　钟　表　*British Clocks and Watches*

The Good Wish Object used to be a popular traditional Chinese gift item. Whenever an emperor ascended the throne, or an empress celebrated her birthday or on the occasion of a major celebration, ministers and generals would present the ruler or the empress with such an object. This practice was most popular during the Qing Dynasty.

The handle of this Good Wish Object was made in Guangdong. At one end is a two-hand British-made watch. At the other end is a compass. The middle section of the object is covered with a piece of glass, under which is a painting of flowers and grass.

如意是一种象征吉祥的礼品，每逢皇帝即位、帝后生日或喜庆时，王公大臣都要向帝后敬献如意。清代极为流行。

此柄如意为中国广东制造。如意头所嵌二针小表为英国制造，尾部中央嵌有一指南针，腰部有嵌珠口长方形的玻璃蒙子，里边有花卉画。

120
Gilded Copper Saddle Watch Inlaid with Decorative Stones

*Made in the 18th century, Britain
9.6cm in diameter,
5cm thick*

铜镀金镶料石口马鞍表
18 世纪
英国制造
表径9.6厘米，厚5厘米

TThe horse saddle wrapped with green sharkskin and fastened with golden nails was for the exclusive use of the emperor. In the middle of the front of the saddle is a two-hand gilded copper watch, the circumference of which is inlaid with red and green gemstones.

　　绿鲨鱼皮金钉马鞍是皇帝专用的，马鞍正中嵌铜镀金二针小表，表的边口周围嵌红绿料石，富贵华丽。

121
**Gilded Copper
Pavilion Clock**

*Made in the 19th
century, France
53 x 29 x 12cm*

铜镀金亭式钟
19 世纪末
法国制造
53 × 29 × 12 厘米

法 国 钟 表　　*French Clocks and Watches*

This clock has a three-hand dial and an open pendulum. The striking system does not rely on a bell but on steel strips.

此钟造型明快，具有超前的设计意识。三针二套明摆时钟，能走时、报时。报时装置不是用钟碗，而是锤打钢条。

122

**Gilded Copper
Enamel Clock**

*Made at the end of the
19th century, France
By Sennet Freres
42 x 31 x 19cm*

铜镀金珐琅座钟
19 世纪末
法国 Sennet Freres 制造
42 × 31 × 19 厘米

French Clocks and Watches 法 国 钟 表

The gilded copper body of the clock is decorated with enamel thread symbolizing flowers. The dial has a picture of an angel. Below the dial is an oblong enamel painting of Our Lady and an angel. Both the dial and the painting are surrounded with green gemstones. This clock was one of the cherished possessions of Dowager Empress Ci Xi.

钟体为铜镀金嵌花卉纹掐丝珐琅，二针二套时钟，钟盘上画有小天使。盘下椭圆形的珐琅画以圣母和小天使为题材。钟盘和珐琅画周围都嵌有绿料石。此钟华贵大方，是宫廷帝后十分喜欢的钟表。

123
Clock with Goddess Holding a Ball

Made in the 19th century, France 58cm high, with a 14 x 14cm stand

铜镀金女神举球钟
19 世纪
法国制造
通高 58 厘米
底座 14 × 14 厘米

法 国 钟 表 *French Clocks and Watches*

The copper goddess holds a bow in her left hand and a ball-shaped clock in her right hand. By the side of the ball is a two-hand dial. The ball is joined to a pendulum through a copper ring. The mechanical parts are inside the ball. When the clock is activated, the pendulum shakes and the copper ring moves, but the ball remains still.

铜铸的女神像左手握弓箭，右手高举一球形摆钟。球的一侧有一二针钟，球的半径处有一铜环和钟摆相连，球内有机芯。当钟表启动后，钟摆晃动，铜环也晃动，球体则不动。

124
Gilded Copper Pavilion Clock Inlaid with Enamel Decorations

Made in the 19th century, Paris
By L. Vrard
54cm high, 24cm in diameter

铜镀金嵌珐琅圆亭式座钟
19世纪
法国巴黎L·Vrard 制造
高54厘米 直径24厘米

French Clocks and Watches 法 国 钟 表

The surface of the gilded copper body is decorated with colorful enamel strips. The mechanical parts are visible behind glass. The pendulum of this three-hand clock is regulated by the flow of mercury.

The L. Vrard Company of France set up a shop in Shanghai in 1860, specially to sell luxurious French-made clocks. It opened two subsidiaries in Tianjin and Beijing, respectively, in 1872 and 1881.

铜镀金钟体表面饰以彩色镂花珐琅片，四周安装有玻璃，可看到机芯。机芯是以发条带动齿轮系统，注水银调节摆，三针钟，能报时。

法国 L·Vrard 公司，于1860年在上海设立，专门销售法国制造的豪华钟。约于1872年和1881年先后在天津与北京建分公司。

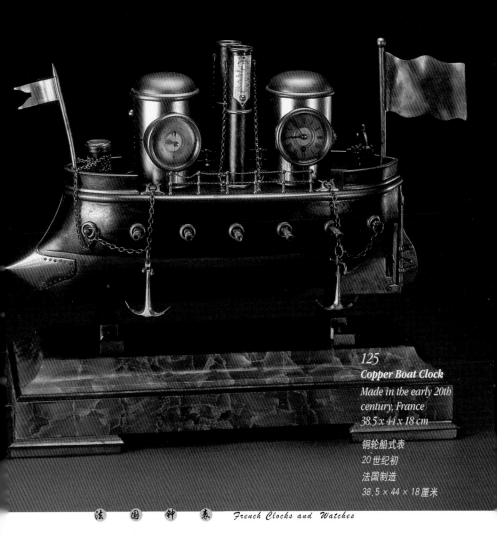

125
Copper Boat Clock
Made in the early 20th century, France
38.5 x 44 x 18 cm

铜轮船式表
20世纪初
法国制造
38.5 × 44 × 18厘米

法 国 钟 表　*French Clocks and Watches*

The marble stand supports a boat, the deck of which supports two pillars. Each of the pillars is inlaid with a dial, one for the minutes and hours and the other for indicating wind and rain conditions. The chimney holds a thermometer. A compass is placed flat on top of the chimney. The helm of the boat serves as the switch to activate the clock.

大理石的底座，轮船甲板两圆柱的正面分别嵌有二针表和风雨表，烟囱上有温度计，烟囱顶上平放指南针，前有一舵，是开关。

126
Copper Locomotive Clock

Made in the early 20th century, France
46.2 x 51.5 x 24cm

铜火车头式表
20世纪初
法国制造
46.2 × 51.5 × 24 厘米

French Clocks and Watches 法 国 钟 表

On a piece of black marble rest two copper rails supporting a copper locomotive. The door of the driver's cabin bears a two-hand dial with two winding holes. The steam furnace has a wind and rain meter. The chimney has a thermometer, while behind the furnace is a copper bell. When the clock is activated, the locomotive moves forward on its rails.

　　黑色大理石座上固定着两条铜轨，上置铜制的火车头。驾驶室的门上嵌一二针表，表盘上有两个上弦孔，蒸汽锅炉的一面有一风雨表，烟囱上嵌一温度计，锅炉后部有一铜铃。当机械开动时，表走，火车头可在轨道上行驶。

127
Copper Furnace Clock

Made in the early 20th century, France
36 x 15 x 15cm

铜锅炉式表
20世纪初
法国制造
36 × 15 × 15厘米

法 国 钟 表 *French Clocks and Watches*

On the copper furnace door is a two-hand dial, which in turn holds a wind and rain meter. On one side of the furnace is a thermometer. The chimney is crowned with a ball which can revolve.

铜质，锅炉炉门上嵌有二针表，表盘上方嵌一风雨表，炉的一侧有一温度计，炉顶有两球，可以转动，以控制速度的快慢。

128
Parrot Clock

*Made in the 19th
century, France
16cm high, with a stand
32cm in diameter*

鹦鹉钟
19 世纪
法国制造
高 16 厘米
底座直径 32 厘米

French Clocks and Watches　　法　国　钟　表

The wooden stand contains the mechanical parts and has a two-hand dial. The cross on the stand supports a ring on which a parrot is perching.

When fully wound up, the mechanical parts produce a sound like a bird singing, while the parrot opens its mouth, and shakes its head and tail.

　　木底座内有机械装置，座前有二针钟，座上的铜十字架上有一圆环。一只制作得十分逼真的鹦鹉栖息于圆环上。

　　上弦后，机械启动发出鸟鸣声，同时鹦鹉张嘴，摆头，抖动尾巴，时针也走动。

129
Chiming Clock Decorated with Enamel Thread
Made in the 19th century, France
16.5 x 8 x 9.5cm

掐丝珐琅八音表
19世纪
法国制造
16.5 × 8 × 9.5厘米

法　国　钟　表　　*French Clocks and Watches*

The gilded copper stand is decorated with enamel thread. Inside the stand are the mechanical parts for the music. There are two oblong-shaped clock dials, one for indicating the minutes and hours, and the other for measuring the air and wind pressure. Between the two dials is a Fahrenheit thermometer whose dial contains a compass. The handle makes it easy to move the clock.

铜镀金掐丝珐琅底座，底座内有八音乐鸣机械。底座上有两个椭圆形表，一个是二针时、分表，一个是风力气压表；两表之间是一华氏温度计；温度计上的圆盘中有一指南针，上有提手，便于携带。

130
Gilded Copper Clock with Rolling Ball Mechanism

Made in the early 19th century, France
53 x 29 x 25cm

铜镀金滚球压力钟
19世纪初
法国制造
53 × 29 × 25厘米

French Clocks and Watches 法 国 钟 表

The top part of the clock is a box with a handle carved in the shape of a lion. The box contains 18 steel balls, each weighing 250 grams. The clock does not rely on a spring, but receives energy from the pressure of the balls to activate the movement. Behind the movement is a large wheel divided into 12 sections. The bottom of the clock has a drawer for receiving the fallen balls. When four balls enter the divided parts on the wheel, it will start revolving. Then the fifth ball will roll onto the wheel, adding pressure to the wheel to make it turn clockwise. The wheel then activates a gear, which activates the pendulum. The balls gradually fall onto the wheel, six at any given time. After the clock works for 16 hours, a ball will fall into the drawer at the bottom, and a new ball will roll onto the wheel to replace it. Every other eight-day period, a fallen ball will be placed back into the box at the top to keep the clock going without interruption. On one side, the clock has a thermometer, and below the dial is a wind and rain meter.

As early as 1595, Europeans began to use rolling balls to activate clocks. This clock is the only one of its kind in the Forbidden City, and thus a rare piece in the collection.

钟的上部是一盒，雕饰的雄狮是盒盖的提手，盒内储有十八个钢球，每个重250克。二针时钟，没有发条，以钢球的压力为动源，带动机芯运转。机芯后部有一个大轮，轮盘周围分为十二个格。钟底有一抽屉，供存放滚下的钢球。当四个钢球进入格内，大轮盘就可转动；第五个钢球起按顺序从盒底圆孔滚入轮盘，钢球使轮盘受压，产生偏心力，向顺时针方向转动；轮盘触动齿轮，带动机芯摆轮摆动走时。钢球陆续滚入轮盘，最多为六个。钟运行16个小时后，有一个钢球落入下层的抽屉里，再由上边盒内滚入一球补充。每隔一周或8天将落入抽屉内的钢球放回上边盒里，这样循环使用，使钟表持续运转。钟表的一侧附有温度计，钟盘下面有一风雨表。

早在1595年，欧洲就利用球体滚动作为钟的动力源，并称之为永恒运动原理。这座压力钟是清宫现存唯一球体压力钟，无为珍贵。

131
Gilded Copper Singing Bird Clock
Made at the end of the 19th century, France
57 x 29 x 19cm

铜镀金鸟音座钟
19 世纪末
法国制造
57 × 29 × 19 厘米

French Clocks and Watches   法 国 钟 表

The stand is decorated with figures made of enamel strips. On the stand is a box with bas-relief sculptured figures and flowers in gilded copper. The center displays a painting, in front of which is a bird on a rock. Higher up, there is a two-hand dial with a visible pendulum. The mechanical parts for controlling the music are in the stand. When fully wound, music is played, followed by the singing of a bird, as the bird opens its mouth and shakes its head and tail.

钟的底座周围嵌绘有人物的珐琅片。座上为布景箱，四周有铜镀金浮雕人物、花卉等，中间嵌一布景画，画前山石中有一只颜色艳丽的小鸟。布景箱顶部有一只二针两套明摆钟，底座有控制音乐鸟鸣的机械，上弦启动后，乐声与鸟鸣先后响起，小鸟也随之张嘴，摇头摆尾。

132
Gilded Copper Clock with Blue Enamel Flower Vase

Made in the early 19th century, France
56 x 35 x 23cm, 24cm in diameter

铜镀金蓝瓷花瓶式钟
19世纪初
法国制造
56 × 35 × 23厘米
钟径24厘米

法　国　钟　表　*French Clocks and Watches*

The two sides of the clock have ears, with a human head and ram's horns. The clock's bottom is decorated with grass and flower patterns. The belly of the ball-shaped vase is highly decorative.

瓶的两侧装饰有人首羊角的双耳,钟面底部饰以卷草纹和花卉纹,球形瓶腹上有二针时针,顶上饰以双耳环,是一件精美工艺品。

133
*Gilded Copper Roll-
ing Ball Clock*
*Made in the early 19th
century, France*
13cm in diameter

铜镀金滚钟
19世纪初
法国制造
表直径 13 厘米

French Clocks and Watches　　法　国　钟　表

This is a highly sophisticated two-hand clock placed on a sloping board at a 10-degree angle. It is not spring-activated, but the movement of the clock as it rolls down the board engages the gear system and thus the pendulum. The clock's movement along the 55-cm-long board takes a total of 24 hours. As a result, the clock has to be replaced at the top of the board once a day.

　　这是一件十分别致的二针圆钟，置放于 10°角的坡板上，可以沿着坡板下滚。没有发条，圆钟内部中心处装有一个小轮，机芯的两夹板左右各装一坠砣，机芯的偏心轮与钟内力轮相接触，机芯在坠砣的重力作用下，没有随钟套下滚，却保持了垂直。这样产生的力，使机芯的偏心轮与圆套内的小轮发力给机芯的齿轮系统，通过齿轮带动钟摆摆动。钟沿坡板下滚，坡板长 55 厘米，由顶端滚至末端需 24 小时，因此，须每天往高处放一次。

　　此钟无论滚到什么位置，"12"与"6"两标站立着一铜镀金鹧鸪。钟套两夹板边沿有细微的齿道，以增加与坡板间的摩擦力，防止从板上滑下。

134
**Gilded Copper
Hand-held Mirror
Clock**

*Made in the 18th
century, Paris
The handle is 3.4 cm
long and the clock is
3.5cm in diameter.*

铜镀金镶料石花把镜表

18 世纪

法国巴黎制造

把镜长 32 厘米

表径 3.5 厘米

法　国　钟　表　　*French Clocks and Watches*

The mirror holder and the handle are of gilded copper bearing patterns of flowers and grass and inlaid with colorful gemstones. The front side is a dressing mirror. At the tip of the mirror is a two-hand clock. On the back of the movement case is the word "Paris". The handle contains an adjustable telescope.

镜托及把柄为铜镀金,上面布满花草纹饰并嵌镶各色料石,为梳妆用把镜。正面为镜子,镜上面的花环中间嵌一块二针表。机芯后板上刻有"PARIS"字样。镜的把柄内装一个单筒可调式望远镜,柄端有盖,可以开合。

135
Air Balloon Clock
*Made at the end of the
19th century, France
6 0 x16 x 16 cm*

气球载人钟
19世纪末
法国制造
60 × 16 × 16厘米

French Clocks and Watches 法 国 钟 表

In 1783, France was the first country to fly a manned hot-air balloon.

The pillar supporting the clock, the balloon serving as the dial of the clock and the rope are all made of copper. The mechanism is contained in the balloon.

公元1783年法国第一次气球载人飞行成功，此钟即为表现这一事件而制。

支撑钟体的圆柱、充作钟盘的球体，以及网绳都是铜制的。下坠的筐底有坠砣，机芯安置在球体内。

136
Gilded Copper
Painted Clock with
Blue Ceramic Vase

Made in the 20th
century, Paris
50 x 33 x 33cm,
12cm in diameter

铜镀金饰彩绘蓝瓷瓶钟
20世纪
法国巴黎制造
50 × 33 × 33 厘米
钟径 12 厘米

法 国 钟 表 *French Clocks and Watches*

The body of the clock is in the shape of a painted blue ceramic vase. The bottom, two handles and rim are decorated with openwork flower and grass patterns in gilded copper. The two-hand dial is inlaid on the belly of the vase. The word "Paris" is found on the back.

钟体为一彩绘蓝瓷瓶，瓶的底座、双耳、上口配饰铜镀金镂空花草纹，古雅华贵。二针时钟嵌于瓶腹，钟机的后板上刻有 PARIS 字样。

137
Cicada-shaped Pin Watch Inlaid with Diamonds

Made at the end of the 19th century, Switzerland
The cicada shape is 5.2cm long and 2.5 cm wide, and the watch is 0.8 cm in diameter.

金嵌钻石蝉形别针表
19世纪末
瑞士制造
蝉长5.2厘米
宽2.5厘米
表径0.8厘米

Swiss Clocks and Watches 瑞 士 钟 表

The gilded case is shaped like a cicada, the wings and head of which are inlaid with diamonds. Its eyes are made of rubies. The handle for winding the watch is on the tail of the insect. In normal conditions, the cicada's wings are closed to cover the watch. A light touch of the handle will spread the wings to reveal a two-hand dial. The watch can be pinned to the chest or held in the pocket on a chain.

金壳，蝉造型，蝉的翅膀和头部嵌有钻石，蝉眼嵌红宝石。表把在尾部，可用来上弦。平时双翅合起来，遮住表，轻轻摁一下表把双翅展开，露出二针小表。蝉的腹部有别针，嘴部有环。可以别在胸前，又可以用链条系挂，携带十分方便，是装饰性的表。

138
Black lacquer and
Gold Painted Tower
Clock
Made at the end of the
19th century
Switzerland
By Pierre Bouet

The body is a tower structure in black lacquer with gold paint. The stand contains the musical mechanism. The door in the center bears a three-hand dial. The keyholes for activating the mechanical parts for the music is on the left side of the stand. The clock is wound from the back.

钟体为一黑漆描金小洋楼模型, 模型底座内有音乐机械, 正中门上嵌有一三针钟。开启音乐机械的弦孔在底座的左侧, 钟表在时钟的背面上弦。

139
Gilded Copper Pocket Watch with Enamel Flower Decorations

Made in the 19th century, Switzerland Edouard Bovet 5.5cm in diameter, 1.2cm thick

铜镀金镶珠口边珐琅花卉怀表
19世纪
瑞士爱德华·播威
(Edouard Bovet)制造
表直径5.5厘米
厚1.2厘米

Swiss Clocks and Watches 瑞 士 钟 表

This is a three-hand pocket watch belonging to Empress Dowager Ci Xi. The edge of the case and the ring are inlaid with pearls. The back cover has colorful flower patterns. The watch is wound with the attached key.

三针怀表。表壳前后边沿和表环都嵌有珍珠。表后盖嵌有颜色鲜艳的各种花卉。此表用钥匙上弦。此表华丽高雅，为帝后用品。

140
Gilded Copper Six-pillar Pavilion Clock

Made at the end of the 19th century, Switzerland
By J. Ullmann
42 x 25 x 15 cm

铜镀金珐琅六柱亭式钟
19世纪末
瑞士　乌利文
(J·Ullmann) 制造
42 × 25 × 15 厘米

The front and back of the clock have glass doors, between which is a two-hand dial with red and white gemstones on the circumference. The keyhole is on the dial. The upper part of the dial displays the words "J. Ullmann & Co", and the lower part, "Hong Kong," indicating that the watch was produced by Ullmann's subsidiary in Hong Kong. Below the dial is a pendulum.

　　钟的前后有玻璃门，内为二针表盘，表盘四周嵌有红、白两色料石，钟能走时、报时，表盘最上正中有一孔，可以调试快慢。表盘上有"J·Ullmann & cie"字样，表盘下方有"Hong Kong"等字样，由此可见此钟为乌利文公司在香港设立的分公司制造。表盘下方是一个圆摆。

141
Gilded Copper Marble Pavilion Clock

Made in the early 20th century, Switzerland
By J. Ullmann
57 x 21 x 21cm

铜镀金石座亭式水法表
20世纪初
瑞士　乌利文
(J·Ullmann)制造
57 × 21 × 21 厘米

Swiss Clocks and Watches 瑞士钟表

The clock sits on a marble stand, and has two dials; the top one is a clock dial with two hands, while the lower one is a thermometer. Images of four men support the pavilion on top of the clock. In the middle is a fountain. When the clock is activated, water cascades like a waterfall.

　　此表为大理石座。座上有两个表盘，上部是二针表盘，下部是寒暑表。表的上方座上雕塑着四人作托举亭顶状。中间是一水法连接钟机，当钟启动后，水法如流水下注。

142
Pocket Watch Inlaid with Pearls

Made in the 19th century, Switzerland By Landor Locle 5.2cm in diameter, 1.9cm thick

金珐琅镶珠怀表
19世纪
瑞士　拉德尔·洛克勒
(Landor Locle)制造
表径5.2厘米
厚1.9厘米

瑞　士　钟　表　*Swiss Clocks and Watches*

This watch's three hands are inlaid with pearls, as is the rim of the watch. The watch is wound by means of the small handle furnished with a button. When the button is pressed, it activates a spring which strikes the minutes, quarters and hours. The back cover bears a portrait of a lady.

　　金质镶珠口三针表，表针尖端嵌有小钻石。用表把上弦，表把上附有问子，摁下就可打簧报出时、刻、分。机芯以发条为动力源，带动表走时、问时，齿轮带动传动系统，可打簧报时。表壳后嵌有精美的珐琅仕女画。

143
Pearl-inlaid Pocket Watch

*Made in the 19th century, Switzerland
6.4cm in diameter,
1.8cm thick*

珐琅镶珠蕃莲花怀表
19世纪
瑞士制造
表直径6.4厘米
厚1.8厘米

Swiss Clocks and Watches 瑞 士 钟 表

This is a three-hand watch, with a button which, when pressed, makes the watch chime the minutes, quarters and hours. The watch also has an elegant key.

三针打簧表，带问子。有精致的上弦的钥匙。上弦后，摁下问子就可以打时、打刻、打分，便于夜间问知时间。

144
Pearl-rimmed Pocket Watch

Made at the end of the 19th century, Switzerland
By Levy
3.2cm in diameter, 0.8cm thick

铜镀金珐琅珠口怀表
19世纪末
瑞士　利威(Lery)制造
表直径3.2厘米
厚0.8厘米

瑞　士　钟　表　*Swiss Clocks and Watches*

The rim and ring of this two-hand watch are inlaid with pearls. A handle is fixed to the watch for winding. The back cover bears an enamel picture of a lady.

The Levy Company was established in Hong Kong around 1880, and dealt in watches until 1900. Most of the Levy watches came from La Chaux-de fonds in Switzerland.

表盘周沿和表环皆嵌珍珠口，二针，用表把上弦，表壳背面为珐琅持琴仕女肖像画。

利威表行大约于1880年在香港创建，经营钟表至1900年。利威钟表来自瑞士拉绍德封(La chaux-de Fonds)。

145
Pomegranate-shaped Pin Watch with Diamond

Made at the end of the 19th century, Switzerland
The pomegranate is 1.6cm in diameter, and the watch is 1cm in diameter.

金珐琅镶钻石石榴形别针表
19世纪末
瑞士制造
石榴径1.6厘米
表径1厘米

Swiss Clocks and Watches 瑞 士 钟 表

The watch is contained in the lower part of the pomegranate. To wind the watch, the upper half is turned clockwise.

　　石榴下部嵌一小表。石榴形的表体是由上下两个半球形拤合而成，上弦时只须按顺时针方向转动上部的半球。

146
Lock-shaped Watch Decorated with Enamel Thread

Made in the 19th century, Switzerland 3cm in diameter, 1.2cm thick

铜镀金掐丝珐琅镶珠锁
形表
19世纪
瑞士制造
锁径3厘米 厚1.2厘米

This watch has a two-hand dial and a keyhole for winding it. The back cover bears an enamel picture, symbolizing opening the gate of knowledge.

The rendering of the enamel thread on the case was an unusual process. First, copper threads are applied to the copper base to create patterns, and then the spaces between the threads are filled with colorful enamel before the baking process. This art, known as cloisonne, is a mixture of the Chinese and Western artistic traditions.

打开表盖露出两针表，盘上有用钥匙上弦的孔。机芯以发条为动力，带动走时齿轮传动系统。表壳后面是一幅儿童手持钥匙的珐琅画，寓意打开知识之门。

这件表壳上的掐丝珐琅的工艺不同于常见的用珐琅釉彩绘画的工艺，而是在铜胎上，用铜丝掐焊出纹样，然后在纹样间填充各色珐琅釉，再经烧制而成，这就是中国的景泰蓝工艺，小小表壳体现了中西文化的交融。

147
Watch Inlaid in Gilded Copper Vase

Made in the 19th century, Switzerland
By Flerier Juvet
The vase is 19.7 x 8.3 x 8cm, and the watch is 3.5 cm in diameter.

铜镀金座珐琅双耳瓶嵌表
19世纪
瑞士 弗勒里耶·有威
(Flearier Juvet)制造
瓶19.7×8.3×8厘米
表径3.5厘米

Swiss Clocks and Watches 瑞 士 钟 表

The belly of the enamel vase bears a two-hand watch. The vase, with peacock feather patterns, is inlaid with pearls and rubies, and an enamel picture of a shepherdess. Below are two movable doors for winding and turning a bird song on and off. The watch is wound by turning the lid of the vase.

The son of Edouard Juvet kept a workshop in Switzerland from 1848 to 1891, producing Juvet brand watches for export to China.

珐琅瓶腹部嵌二针表。小瓶为孔雀翎眼花纹的珐琅瓶，嵌米珠和红宝石。瓶腹后面有牧羊女珐琅画，下方有两处活门，可以上弦和播放鸟音，瓶盖为上弦的钥匙。

爱德华·播威的儿子于1848－1891年在瑞士开设钟表店，专门制造出口中国的表，品牌为"有威"(Juvet)。

148
Copper Windmill Clock

Made in the early 20th century
By Hangry
77cm high, 36cm in diameter

铜风车钟
20世纪初
亨德利
高77厘米　直径36厘米

The stand is furnished with a door and windows. Behind the door is the mechanical system. The lighthouse has a dial and a wind and rain meter. On the side is a Fahrenheit thermometer. On top of the clock are windmill vanes, which can turn. The very top of the lighthouse has a weathervane bearing the English words "north," "south," "east" and "west."

When the clock is activated, the windmill starts to turn.

　　钟为灯塔式，铜质，底部有门和窗，门里有机械装置，打开后可以上弦。塔壁上有两针时钟和风雨表，侧面有一华氏温度计。上部有风车翼，可以转动。塔顶有风向标和指向针，指向针上有英文东西南北标志。

　　启动后，风翼转动，表走时。

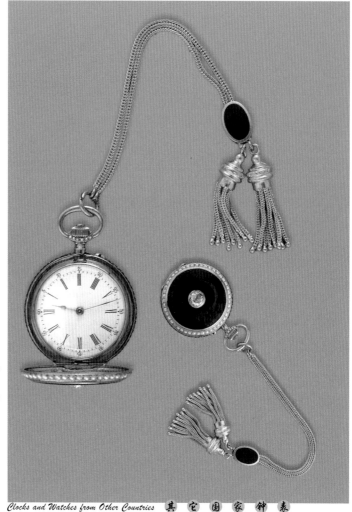

149
Small Gold Watch

Made in the early 20th century
By Hangry 3.3cm in diameter, 0.8cm thick

小金表
20世纪初
亨德利
直径3.3厘米
厚0.8厘米

The Hangry Company was first established in 1864, to deal in Swiss watches and German clocks. By the 1930s, it had opened 30 shops and factories in major cities in China.

This is a 18-K gold watch, the blue enamel case cover of which has a diamond in the middle and a ring of pearls on the rim. The chain is made of threaded gold.

亨德利创建于1864年(清朝同治三年)，专门经营瑞士表和德国钟表，至20世纪30年代，在中国各大城市设立的分店及工厂约有三十家。

此金表为18K金，蓝珐琅表壳中心镶有钻石，表周围嵌有一圈珍珠，表链为金丝编织而成，高雅珍贵。

150
Gilded Copper Singing Bird Clock

*Made at the end of the
19th century
By Hangry
105 x 56 x 35cm*

铜镀金鸟音座钟
19 世纪末
亨德利
105 × 56 × 35 厘米

其 它 国 家 钟 表　*Clocks and Watches from Other Countries*

The clock has a three-hand enamel dial, below which there are two smaller dials, respectively for turning the music on and off and for changing the tunes. A picture on the dial shows a green singing bird in the woods. The stand is a Chinese product.

此钟为三针珐琅盘，盘的下面左右两侧有两个小盘，一个是换乐盘，一个是打止乐盘。钟盘上有一布景，树林中有一只可鸣叫的翠鸟。钟的底座是另配的中国制品。

151
Glass-cased Gilded Copper Clock

Made in the early 20th century, New York, USA
42 x 22 x 19cm

铜镀金四明钟
20 世纪初
美国纽约制造
42 × 22 × 19厘米

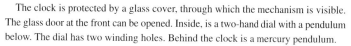

Clocks and Watches from Other Countries 其它国家钟表

The clock is protected by a glass cover, through which the mechanism is visible. The glass door at the front can be opened. Inside, is a two-hand dial with a pendulum below. The dial has two winding holes. Behind the clock is a mercury pendulum.

　　钟座和顶部雕有卷草纹饰，线条清晰流畅。钟身的四面嵌有玻璃，可透视钟芯，前边的玻璃门可以打开。里面为二针钟盘，中间是一明卡摆轮，钟盘上有二孔，可以上弦。钟后有下垂的水银摆。

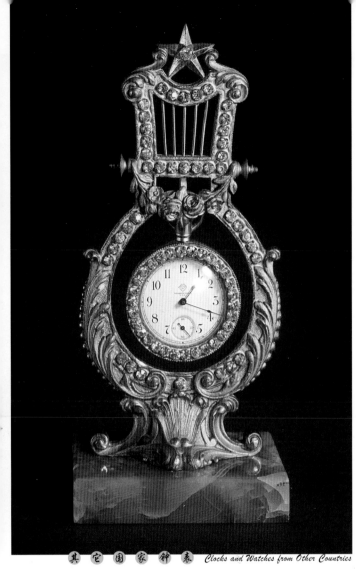

152
Gilded Copper Clock Inlaid with Artificial Diamonds
Made in the early 20th century, New York, USA
22 x 10 x 7cm, 5cm in diameter

铜镀金嵌假钻石表
20世纪初
美国纽约制造
22 × 10 × 7厘米
表直径5厘米

其它国家钟表 *Clocks and Watches from Other Countries*

The stand is a piece of light green marble on which stands a gilded copper frame from which is suspended a two-hand dial. The lower part of the dial has a small dial for reading the seconds. The frame and the big dial are inlaid with artificial diamonds.

　　此表底座为淡绿色大理石，座上竖立一琵琶形铜镀金表架，架中间悬挂着一块二针小表，表盘下方有一小秒盘。表架和表盘周围嵌有用玻璃仿制的钻石。

153
Gilded Copper Clock on Horseback

Made about 1770
Italy
83 x 45 x 37cm

铜镀金转水法人物马驮
钟
约1770年
意大利制造
83 × 45 × 37厘米

Clocks and Watches from Other Countries 其它国家钟表

The gilded copper stand contains the mechanical parts. The decorations in the front include a fountain, human figures, a dolphin, exotic beasts and shells. On the terrace of the stand is a giant horse carrying two comic figures from Italian opera. They hold a clock dial which has smaller dials for indicating the hours, minutes, seconds, and lunar and solar calendar months. Under the canopy at the top is a figure holding a hammer for striking a bell. When the clock is activated, a fountain turns, to produce a cascading waterfall, the figures prance forward and a butterfly under the horse's belly flaps its wings, all to the accompaniment of music.

　　铜镀金座，底层内有机械装置，正面布景内有水法，景前有人物、海豚、怪兽、贝壳等。底座平台立一匹高大骏马，马背上有二位意大利喜剧人物。上部为钟盘，钟盘正中有一秒针，上下左右有四个小盘，分别为时盘、秒盘、阴历月盘和阳历月盘。顶端的伞盖下有一手持锤敲钟的人。当机械启动后，在音乐声中水法转动犹如瀑布，景前的活动人物跳舞前进，马腹下的彩蝶扇动翅膀。

154
Gilded Copper
Twin-dog Clock
Made in the early 20th
century
Japan
17 x 13 x 5.5cm

铜镀金双狗座钟
20世纪
日本制造
17 × 13 × 5.5厘米

On the gilded copper stand is a two-hand clock which is wound from behind. Two hunting dogs lean against the clock. Its shape, decoration and the mechanical structure indicate that it is a typical early 20th century product.

The backboard of the movement has winding and readjustment buttons.

　　铜镀金钟座的上部是一二针时钟，在后面上弦，两只猎狗依偎着圆钟，形象十分逼真，从外形和工艺水平以及机械结构看是二十世纪的产品。

　　机芯后板上有上弦纽，另有调速快慢针以及拨时、分针纽。

图书在版编目（CIP）数据

清宫钟表集萃：北京故宫珍藏／廖频编；郎秀华，秦小培撰；
胡锤，刘志岗，赵山摄．－北京：外文出版社，2002.8
ISBN 978-7-119-03050-0

Ⅰ.清… Ⅱ.①廖… ②郎… ③秦… ④胡… ⑤刘… ⑥赵…
Ⅲ.钟表－考古－中国－清代 Ⅳ.K875.2

中国版本图书馆 CIP 数据核字（2002）第 023441 号

编　　辑：廖　频
撰　　文：郎秀华　秦小培
图　　片：故宫博物院提供
摄　　影：胡　锤　刘志岗　赵　山　赵小权
　　　　　冯　辉　夏　静　邹一伟　余志勇等
翻　　译：黄友义　丛国玲　郝光峰
英文改稿：保罗·怀特
设　　计：兰佩瑾　元　青
责任编辑：兰佩瑾

清宫钟表集萃

© 外文出版社
外文出版社出版
（中国北京百万庄大街24号）
邮政编码：100037
外文出版社网址：http://www.flp.com.cn
外文出版社电子邮件地址：info@flp.com.cn
sales@flp.com.cn
深圳市佳信达印务有限公司印刷
中国国际图书贸易总公司发行
（中国北京车公庄西路35号）
北京邮政信箱第399号　邮政编码 100044
2002年（大32开）第一版
2008年第一版第二次印刷
（英汉）
ISBN 978-7-119-03050-0
09600（平）
85-E-528P